DREAMSTATE
A Conspiracy Theory

JED MCKENNA

Dreamstate: A Conspiracy Theory

By Jed McKenna

Print ISBN: 978-0-9891759-7-5
E-Book ISBN: 978-0-9891759-8-2
Audiobook ISBN: 978-0-9891759-9-9

Contents

Reality, what a concept.

Robin Williams

The Party at the House in the Evening

How can you determine whether at this moment we are
sleeping, and all our thoughts are a dream; or whether we
are awake, and talking to one another in the waking state?

Plato, Theaetetus

L ISABELLE MUST HAVE INVITED ME to attend a small party
she's hosting for some friends and workmates because I
am standing at her door with a gift when she opens it like a
normal person and invites me into her brightly lighted and
sparkly home. I take her coat and hand her my red propeller.

"These are my friends Fredwin and Latrina," says Lisabelle
in our secret language.

"Oh, yes," I nod.

"This is my Jedwin," Lisabelle explains to Fredwin and Latrina, "he says things."

"Oh," says Latrina, "my."

"Latrina," I say, "any relation to the toilet?"

"Oh no," she says, "just friends."

"And you, Fredwin?"

"Cornpigs," says Fredwin. "I'm in cornpigs. Full body, non-synthetic, top of the line." He leans forward and whispers to me, "We sit on the *good* side of the table."

"Don't I know it," I say and pat his arm. "I must go."

"Come with me now," says Lisabelle and ushers me to the back patio, past the hot tub where Michael Jackson calls me by the wrong name, to another couple.

"Jedwin," says Lisabelle, "here is Bradwin and wife Sugarbelle. I work on Sugarbelle at the plant on Tuesday. Bradwin is just like you."

"Oh," I say.

"Jedwin does stuff," says Lisabelle.

"Oh, yes," says Bradwin. "I had an uncle."

"It's all so shiny," says Sugarbelle.

"What stuff?" asks Bradwin.

"I play golf, Bradwin. A *lot* of golf."

We enjoy a hearty laugh.

"And you, Bradwin? What, huh?"

"Creature comforts," says Bradwin with a wink. "I think you know."

"Very," I wink back and wonder if I'm sleepy.

"Are you doing stuff now?" asks Sugarbelle.

"I'm not sure," I say. "Do you mean *now* now or now *now*?"

"Very," she says.

There are many people at this party so I look at them. There is Tedwin who I know from the car crash and there's Mr. Rourke in a white suit greeting people by the smoky hibachi where Sydney Greenstreet in a white suit turns the noodles.

"Oh," I say gladly, "I know Sydney."

Or maybe I'm thinking of Whoopi Goldberg in a white suit who now takes over the noodles.

"Sorry," I say, but no one answers and I am alone.

I look for someone to stand with and see young Elliot Gould for whom I have fondness. He wears an army field jacket, mirrored sunglasses and a drooping black moustache.

"Great party," he says without moving his lips.

"Very," I agree.

"Story in a dream," he says.

"Dream in a story in a story in a dream," I reply. "In a dream," I add, not confident that I have spoken accurately.

He nods without moving his head.

"Funny stuff," one of us says.

If the scuba guy in the pool is a toy he's a very good one. I am quietly pleased with the lighting arrangements. I remember something that never happened but now it did. From an upper balcony a voice can be heard, and the mysterious sizzling of noodles.

"Boy," I say, making party banter, "nothing like a good lozenge."

No one replies.

"Something should happen now," I say without words and a bodiless voice tells me it's okay.

"Oh, good," I say.

"Can I get you something?" the voice asks.

"Headphones," I say, "and a fanbelt."

The bodiless voice goes away and I am glad.

"Hello," says a man I can't bring into focus, "my name is Jedwin."

"Hello Jedwin," I say, "my name is also Jedwin."

"No," he says, "*Jed*win."

"Oh," I say, "you mean *Chad*win."

"That's what I said," he says.

There is something in the air. The light sparkles in my vision and I wonder if I'm missing something. The music has the dull whump-whump of an out-of-tune steamboat. I remember that I suffer from hydromyandria and am sad but proud. The dancing stops before it begins. Julianne Moore gives me a knowing look and I look back, also knowingly. I wonder what we know.

"You can't get there from here," she whispers.

That's what we know.

I am thirsty so I set down my piece of cardboard. Something is just about to happen, but then it doesn't. I am bored so I do a little dance that I know is quite good. I also know that my hand can pass right through these people but I don't want to do that because I like them a little bit.

"Are you having just the *best* time?" Lisabelle asks me.

I look at her and she looks like my sister the baroness so I look away. The crowd parts and I see why. There is a distant rumble. Something approaches but doesn't arrive. I am still holding the cardboard which, I feel, is explanation enough.

"There is wonder in your eyes," says a sparkly woman next to me.

"I'm not here is why," I reply.

"Well," she says, "any time now."

I agree but don't say so. Something almost happens. I look around to see who else is missing. I can tell the levels are wrong but I mustn't touch the dials. I await the next development and there it is, over in the garden where an angel of white shoots an arrow of light into the night and calls it the winter moon. Mayabelle runs to me and I am so happy. I catch her in mid-air and offer her the red propeller but she chooses my ear instead and we are on the ocean at night and it is dark.

Where I Lived, and What I Lived For

This was an airy and unplastered cabin, fit to entertain
a travelling god, and where a goddess might trail her
garments. The winds which passed over my dwelling were
such as sweep over the ridges of mountains, bearing the
broken strains, or celestial parts only, of terrestrial music.
The morning wind forever blows, the poem of creation is
uninterrupted; but few are the ears that hear it. Olympus is
but the outside of the earth everywhere.

H.D. Thoreau

MAYA AND I ARRIVED HERE right at the end of November.
It was well into fall, all color gone but the green of
the Rhododendrons, the day was gray and rainy. Our cab
driver was happy for the long fare but not so happy with the
last few miles of climbing up a rutted gravel road that only
a serious four-wheel drive vehicle had any business on. In
twenty minutes we made it halfway before he apologetically
began a five-point turnaround. From his GPS he guessed we
were within a mile of the address. We weren't.

We got in the taxi at the place where I dropped off the rental car we'd spent the previous ten hours in. Now the driver offered to take us back down, but Maya and I got out and began the rest of the way on foot. Southern Appalachia is the place, one of the pretty high parts. The air was thin, damp and chilly, but not unpleasant. The fog we walked in was the clouds we'd seen from below, down near the sign that said the state didn't maintain the road past this point. We weren't *high* high, but high for the Eastern U.S. at nearly a mile up.

We walked and explored. I saw claw-ravaged trees and knew that was the work of bears. I also wondered about bobcats, moonshiners, meth cooks, ginseng poachers, timber rattlers and copperheads, and hoped they were all hibernating. Maya sniffed around a bit and occasionally stopped to stare off into the milky white woods, sensing something outside my range, but no one popped out to kill us.

I could see from tracks in the road that only vehicles with aggressive tires came up this far. At one point we walked back and forth up a series of hairpin curves for more the twenty minutes. When we got to the top of the last one I looked down through leafless trees and saw that for all that time and effort, we'd only traveled a few hundred feet. That's when it occurred to me that what a GPS called a mile where it didn't even register a road must mean a mile as the crow flies which, on this twisty-ass road, could be a whole lot more.

Which was fine. I like walking and Maya tolerates it. Some of the slopes were a bit much for both of us. I wasn't carrying water but Maya drank out of the small streams that funneled down every inside curve.

There had been some houses lower down the road, maybe in the first two miles, but after that there were just the occasional *No Trespassing* and *Acreage for Sale* signs nailed to trees. I knew from billboards and real estate magazines that gated mountainside communities with long views, manmade lakes and rolling golf courses were big business here, but we were far above anything like that. Those places had paved and well-maintained roads. I doubted any of those fancy Lexus SUVs and chrome-trimmed Hummer things I'd seen below ever ventured up roads like this.

It was actually late in the day, maybe an hour of light left, and I didn't have a phone, so if we weren't on the right road we could be in a pickle. I wasn't worried, but I was aware. Could I start a fire up here? No. How long would it take us to get down to the nearest house? Two or three hours, maybe longer if it got *dark* dark. I was underdressed and already the damp cold was seeping in. Maya, a Border Collie, is bred for the Scottish Highlands, so she'd survive me. Would she eat my body? I hoped so, but only if she was genuinely hungry, not just peckish, and I hoped she'd wait until I was dead.

The rain ranged from so little that I could barely detect it to a pleasant misting that didn't need me to put up my hoodie hood. For much of the walk we were just ascending through gloomy woods, but once in awhile we'd emerge into an opening and I could tell that if we weren't standing inside a cloud, the view would be pretty awesome.

We finally made it up to where the road ended in a turn-around with two driveways. One was overgrown gravel with no markings, the other had two stone pillars and a steel gate that was open. The mailboxes were miles below. We went the steel gate way and got to the house with a few minutes of light to spare. That was six months ago when Maya and I arrived at Lisa's house for a five day visit.

✿

The other driveway went up to a cabin also on Lisa's property, and that's where Maya and I live now. It's a dump in the best sense. I made some improvements in the early days when I realized I'd be staying awhile, and now I have it set up perfectly for Maya and me.

A few hundred yards below the cabin is Lisa's house, which is a real showstopper. A big, fancy A-frame with decks and a roofed outdoor living room complete with furniture, wet bar, kitchen and fireplace, all overlooking a breath-taking, heart-stopping, vertigo-inducing view of layer after receding layer of Blue Ridge Mountains. The inside of the house is crazy-nice, with thirty foot high windows overlooking the monster view, and a master suite up in a rear loft space that also enjoys the main view. Lisa told me she took a liking to the area during our trip to Virginia together ten years earlier. She wasn't fond of the long drive up, but felt the view and the solitude were more than worth it.

✿

I start my days slowly, ramping up the fire and having coffee and a light meal, then Maya and I set out for a walk. There aren't a lot of nearby trails as such, so in the early days we used animal trails and waterways and did some bush-whacking, but eventually we found our way to the other side of the mountain where an abutting national forest provides plenty of trails and fire roads.

Generally, we're back at the cabin after a few hours, both a little spent. I set up some food for both of us and we stretch out for an hour. Then, if we don't have any errands to run, which we usually don't, I might do some writing in the afternoon. For the first three or four months we were here, I was in lumberjack mode for several hours a day. Between the cabin and the main house there are eleven indoor and outdoor fireplaces, so when we first got here Maya and I went into town and bought a bunch of scary wood cutting stuff; a twenty-inch chainsaw and a dozen related items. Lisa has an old tractor with a log splitter attachment that came with the place, so I was able to put together a pretty nice little firewood operation.

So that's what we did with our afternoons for the mild winter months. Maya wasn't really much help. She didn't care for all the noise and tended to watch from a distance. I didn't have to cut many trees down because the forest was littered with fallen ones in various stages of ripeness. All I had to do was cut, split and haul. In the first two months, I had stocked every fireplace to capacity without leaving Lisa's almost forty acres. Putting myself out of work made me sad so I learned a way to stack round ricks seven or eight feet high so that a ten-by-ten foot plot of ground could store and season all the wood I could process in a week, and now we have a bunch of those scattered around.

"That's more wood then we'll use in the next decade," Lisa said when she saw what I'd been up to.

"I know," I said, "but I'm attached to the activity."

"You're going to keep cutting firewood?"

"I'm attached to the activity," I repeated.

"Then I guess we'll need a big firepit," she said.

So I got to work on that. I cleared and leveled a place in the woods between the house and the cabin. With the heavy lifting done by the guys from the stone yard, I built an eight-foot ring of boulders surrounded by a flagstone patio where I placed green Adirondack chairs and tables made from recycled plastic milk jugs. It was a big project and took six weeks and several thousand dollars of Lisa's money. Sometimes Lisa and I hang out there and drink wine around a big fire, sometimes just me and Maya.

✦

Before I got to the cabin I was re-reading some John le Carré cold war stuff which led to some Stalinist-era stuff which led to some Solzhenitsyn and Shalamov gulag stuff. When that got too heavy, I turned to some humorists I hadn't read in a while; Perelman, Wodehouse, Woody Allen, Ring Lardner, and others. When that got to be too light, I switched to reading plays, I don't remember why. This was around the time I arrived at the cabin and I think I was playing with the idea of life as theater of the absurd, which prompted me to read Martin Esslin's *The Theatre of the Absurd*, which prompted me to read or re-read Beckett, Ionesco, Genet, Stoppard and then Albee, Sartre, and Pinter. I came to the conclusion that, for me, all plays fell into two categories; *Waiting for Godot,* and other.

✦

My first writing project in the cabin started out as a full-length play entitled *Fedallah.* The character Fedallah in the book *Moby-Dick* represents the Mysterious Other; the ancient, fireborn aspect of Ahab, who is, in turn, Melville's own dark psyche personified, which is, in turn, a reflection of our own. In short, Fedallah is the avatar of a surrogate of a proxy representing the reader's own struggle with the reader's own white whale, or something like that.

The one-man, one-set, three-act play would spend one long night with Herman Melville in the study of his upstate New York home, *Arrowhead*, as he struggles to construct his masterpiece while simultaneously deconstructing himself. In my cabin at night, it was very easy to imagine Melville in his study. I used only candles and firelight as I wrote hundreds of pages of notes and covered sections of wall with index cards and storyboard sketches.

The idea called for a very dynamic set. Light and sound and sinister wall shadows would have to transform Melville's quiet study into the deck of the Pequod, the madness of the chase, and the bloody swirling chaos of the kill, but even more, the inside of Melville/Ahab's seething, churning mind. A thunderstorm raging outside would mirror similar storms inside the room and inside the man. Melville would shift between the cool thoughtfulness of the author to the hot mania of a tortured soul writhing in the agony of prolonged self-immolation, all in one dark room on one dark and stormy night. That sorta thing.

When the dawn finally breaks, we find a near-dead Melville at his desk surrounded by a mountain of handwritten pages as he pens the final words about the whale swimming away leaving an orphan behind, and the ocean rolling on as it did five thousand years ago. Curtain.

I didn't take it past the sketch stage, but maybe someday I will. I would have written it to be read, not produced, but I think I lost interest when I saw that, with further work, it's natural evolution would take it from *Fedallah* to *Ahab!*, and eventually to *Ahab! The Musical.*

✿

So I lost interest and burned everything. Instead, I wrote a ten-minute play of a slightly recompiled dialog between Ahab and his first mate that isolates the core of Ahab's conflict. Then I started doodling out some other short plays for my own amusement, and when I stuck a few of them together I found that they completed a nice arc, so I wrapped them up into a seven vignette play and it was published with the title *Play.*

Then, for some forgotten reason, I developed an interest in the future of artificial intelligence. I started with Kurzweil and branched out until I came to the amusing realization that AI would eventually wipe out humanity. How great is that? I mean, you know, *sad*, I suppose, but also pretty funny. We are racing to create a synthetic intelligence that will, without malice or ill-will, either kill us or turn us into livestock. And this isn't just some weird little theory, it might be inevitable, and a lot of smart people are worried about it. So I wrote a short play about that which is offered at no cost from the publisher. My original title was *The Unexpected Upside of French Kissing Your Toaster*, but we changed it to *A Nice Game of Chess,* or *How I Learned to Stop Worrying and Love the Technological Singularity.*

✿

And then I started writing a book about the dreamstate. It didn't start out as a book project; it was just the stuff I was thinking about while walking. I started writing it out to better understand it, and found it to be a challenging and amusing subject. It's weird, though, because the only thing you can say for sure about the dreamstate is that you can't say anything for sure about it, and you can't even say *that* for sure. Or that. But despite the fact that something or nothing may or may not be said about it, there's a lot to say.

✿

The log cabin Maya and I live in is more than eighty years old but was updated in the mid-nineties with decent doors and windows, new appliances, and a green metal roof. It has water from a well, an adequate little kitchen, and an adequate little bathroom with a shower and a stacked washer/dryer unit. Except for the bathroom and closet, it's all one big room. The south-facing windows along the covered front porch are large and let in varying amounts of sunlight depending on season, foliage, and weather. The open interior feels very spacious. The large freestanding stone chimney separates the smaller kitchen from larger living and sleeping area. On the kitchen side of the chimney is a woodburning stove that vents directly into the chimney's flue, and on the living area side is a big fireplace that's not as efficient as the wood stove, but a lot nicer to sit in front of.

The cabin's furniture was acceptable in a first apartment sense, but when I realized I'd be staying awhile I got a new bed, recliner, couch, linens and some other things. The couch, a coffee table, a rocker and the recliner sit in front of the fireplace. There's also a small dining table in the big room where I sometimes write and eat. I also bought a lava lamp. It makes a nice nightlight and makes the cabin feel more groovy than spooky at night, and gives it a cool alien glow from a distance.

✿

Lisa travels around on state business all week but she's usually home on weekends. That's when we get together for a meal or to sit in front of a fire, drink wine and talk. Because of the transition she began during our time together in Mexico ten years earlier, she and I get each other better than either of us get or get got by others.

I seem to be drinking every night. The last person I sat around drinking with was Lisa's father, Frank, when he tried to educate me about single malts and cigars in Mexico. These days it's cheap table wine, hearty red stuff from a jug. My limit is two glasses. If I have three I feel it the next day. I drink at night while I sit in front of the fire, Maya at my feet, and read.

✿

So that's my mountain man existence from fall to spring until one day when, suddenly, there comes a knock upon my door.

16

Where We Are, and How We Got Here

> You are only a disciple because your eyes are closed. The day you open them you will see there is nothing you can learn from me or anyone. What then is a Master for? To make you see the uselessness of having one.

Anthony de Mello

BEFORE I ANSWER THE DOOR, let's make sure we're all on the same page. The central premise of this book is the admittedly ridiculous but incontrovertibly true assertion that the universe does not exist. This is something you can understand conceptually, like watching a documentary about Antarctica, or experientially, like moving to Antarctica. There's also a related phenomenon where you fall asleep watching the documentary and wake up in the frozen wasteland. That's gotta be weird, but the truth is that you're asleep in a barren wasteland dreaming that you're not, so that's where waking up gets you.

✿

We can take a look at the dreamstate concept now so the rest of the book makes more sense. Picture a dead planet; lifeless, featureless, empty. This is your homeworld, and you never left. It's a very inhospitable place, but what's worse, it's boring. Living on this dead rock floating in infinite nothingness would drive anyone batshit crazy in thirty seconds, but you have come up with a very clever solution: You sleep, you dream of a better world, and you inhabit it. Maybe your dream is sweet, maybe nightmarish, probably a bit of both, but it's *way* better than being awake on a dead rock in the middle of nowhere.

See? Conceptually, it's all very simple. Truthworld is a rather dull affair, but Dreamworld is fantastically rich and wonderful, and all we have to do to stay in this wonderland is not pinch ourselves to see if we're dreaming. What could be simpler? All we have to do is stay asleep, and all we have to do to stay asleep is not wake up.

The thing that threatens our repose is thinking. Thinking is something we *can* do and which we believe we *do* do, but which we really *don't* do. Granted, we might think about trifles like crossword puzzles and nuclear fusion and what's for dinner, but it's really best not to think about anything too serious, like the fact that you're not awake at this very moment and whatnot.

But here you are, doing the one thing you're not supposed to be doing. It's like Adam and Eve with the apple; you are given this magnificent paradise to enjoy, and all you have to do in return is not eat the apple, which is exactly what you're trying to do right now. Remember Nietzsche's warning: When you bite into the apple, the apple bites also into you.

✿

Here's how simple this stuff really is. In truth, only two things exist, one of which doesn't. The two things are awareness and appearance. Awareness is consciousness, appearance is the content of consciousness, and everything in your I-universe is one or the other. Consciousness is true, the content of consciousness is not. It doesn't get much simpler than that.

✿

There are three states in which a self-aware being can be. Sub-lucid and lucid *in* the dreamstate, and awake *from* the dreamstate.

The first state, sub-lucid, means eyes-closed or asleep in the dreamstate. That's pretty much everyone. It encompasses a range between not-lucid to almost lucid and equates to pre-pubescence. This is what is meant by born of the flesh. We can also refer to it as Human Childhood or the Segregated State.

The second state, lucid, means eyes-open or awake in the dreamstate. It equates to post-pubescence and very few get this far. This is what is meant by reborn of the spirit or self-born. We can also refer to it as Human Adulthood or the Integrated State.

The third state is awake *from* the dreamstate, which is a different and unrelated paradigm from the dreamstate. Awake from the dreamstate means awake on a dead rock in the middle of nowhere, which is about as much fun as it sounds. It's the only state that merits the term spiritual enlightenment, all other states being imaginary.

✿

I am awake *from* the dreamstate. My eyes are open, which means that I occupy a different paradigm of reality than you; mine having the distinction of not being a lie, yours having a whole lot more entertainment value. I also inhabit the dreamstate. I used to inhabit it as fully and effortlessly as anyone, but these days it takes a bit more effort.

I write books describing what I see and sharing what I know. I am not a guru or a teacher or the head of a spiritual empire. I'm a guy living in a cabin in the woods in the mountains with his dog minding his own business and writing books full of charming run-on sentences because that's what my awake-in-the-dreamstate character does. I don't take my own character too personally, and I avoid those who do.

My assumption is that anyone reading this book wants to be in the Integrated State because I consider it the natural and universally desirable condition for all humans past the age of puberty. However, our failure to develop naturally is actually the success of the mechanism that keeps the dreamstate amusing. While the Integrated State is abundant in awesome qualities, it is lacking in drama and conflict, and that's why it will never catch on. Boredom is the enemy of awareness.

✿

Awaking in or from the dreamstate does not require teachers or traditions or any of that, though ominous horizons and tidal forces compel us toward such safe harbors. The reason popular belief systems are popular is because we secretly want to be seduced and saved from ourselves. Those revered teachings and ideologies don't snatch us off the street and brainwash us; we go to them as if in a trance. We swoon longingly into their embrace, eager to cuddle up to any warm, fluffy guru-doll that lets us stay asleep. Buddhism produces Buddhists, not Buddhas. Ditto all -isms. If you want to be a member of something big and safe and respectable, then the bustling spiritual marketplace is your salvation superstore. If you want to wake up, you're on your own.

✿

The dreamstate we call reality is finite. It has borders and those borders can be crossed with intent, but also by accident. One minute you're snooping around like you're doing right now, and the next minute you find that you've crossed a line without even knowing there *was* a line, and there's no crossing back.

It's like you're asleep on top of a cliff. As long as you stay asleep, you're safe, but as soon as you get antsy and start sleepwalking, things can change in ways that life in the dreamstate has not prepared you for. You walk off the edge and that's it; there's no undo button, no do-overs, no going back. One minute you're sleepwalking in one paradigm, the next minute you're plummeting in another. This can really happen. Sleepwalking is how it happens, and that's what you're doing now. Simply by thinking about your situation, by inquiring, by biting the apple, you risk spontaneous emergence from the sub-lucid dreamstate into desolation. This probably won't happen, but maybe it will.

✿

We are not in belief territory here. I am not trying to

convince you of anything and you are not being asked to believe anything. Accepting that reality is a dream would just be another belief, and no belief is true. Belief is a function of the eyes-closed state, but we're talking about seeing with open eyes.

Spirituality is about staying comfortably asleep in the dreamstate. Waking up *in* the dreamstate might be thought of as trans-spiritual and waking *from* it as anti-spiritual. Neither process requires ideology or doctrine, opinion or belief. You see it or you don't because your eyes are open or they're not. The twist is that it sounds like we're talking about you, but there is no such thing as you. The journey of awakening is the journey to no-self, meaning that self itself is but a dream. So that begs the question, who is all this for? ~~Who's~~ dream is this, and who wants to wake up?

Whose

✿

Okay, now let's see who's at the door.

The Doors of Perception

This whole creation is essentially subjective, and
the dream is the theater where the dreamer is at
once scene, actor, prompter, stage manager, author,
audience, and critic.

C.G. Jung

"WHAT FRESH HELL IS THIS?" I plagiarize before yelling come in. In comes what I expect will be Lisa but is actually Lisa's daughter Maggie, last seen as a delightfully precocious child in Mexico, now a young lady. She has Lisa's almost-blonde hair tied back the way Lisa wears it. She wears tennis shoes, black spandex tights, and a t-shirt that says fifty is the new thirty which I doubt is hers because she's not even twenty. She looks fresh-scrubbed. My guess is that she came back from school with bags of dirty laundry, so she showered and grabbed clean stuff from her mom.

She's not unexpected. I knew I'd be seeing her soon and there are plenty of pictures down at the house, so her appearance was also known. She was home for Christmas but I was in Honduras so we missed each other. I stand up, ready to hug and do the whole last-time-I-saw-you thing, but she races past me and falls on Maya who seems equally happy about the reunion, and I remember that they had been great pals when last they met.

Things settle down and we take our seats. I offer her some peasant wine in a juice glass and she accepts. She's in bubbly spirits, a radically different energy than I'm used to, and which seems perversely out of place in the sedate cabin.

"I've only been up here once before," she says, "it's a lot nicer now. You fixed it up I guess. You don't turn on the lights?"

"I like the fire and candles."

"You're like Jeremiah Johnson or something up here. I hope you come down to the house a lot. Bring Maya. Maybe we can do stuff together, go down to town for lunch or whatever."

"I've been to a town," I say, but she doesn't pick up the reference. "Your mom says you're going to an arts college to become a filmmaker," I say. "How's that going?"

She answers as she pets Maya and we drink our wine. She's actually attending two art schools in some way I don't understand, but the main point is that she's using the schools for her own agenda rather than following a degree path to impress future employers. Instead of spending time and money on pointless requirements, she's cherry-picking the courses, instructors and resources she needs to achieve her own personal goals. That makes a lot more sense to me than the diploma mill and debt route. Get in, get what you need, and get out.

"Do you remember our time in Mexico?" I ask.

"Yeah, some. I remember Maya and the house where we lived and the pool and the dolphin fountain. I remember Grandpa, that was the last time I saw him. I remember your books and how we worked together, mom too, and did those questions for you."

"Some of that made it into the book. I was very grateful for your help."

"Yeah, I read it. That was pretty neat. Are you writing now?"

"No, not really, just for myself. Not much left to say. So what is it you're doing at these schools of yours?"

"Well," she says coyly, "that's kind of something I wanted to talk to you about."

She tells me her plans for a writing project and I nod and consider. Her idea is not totally uninteresting. Eventually, she returns home and I return to my deep thoughts.

☼

Beyond I Am, there is no knowledge to be found in the dreamstate, only anti-knowledge; the knowledge of what's not. Beyond that, I can only interpret abstractions in a way that I find satisfactory, and lay out the available pieces in a way that is not displeasing to look upon. There can be no grand epiphany when studying reality. One can never see the dreamstate clearly because there's really nothing there. I can explain the dreamstate and know that I'm as right as it's possible to be, but it can never rise above the infinite regress of metadream interpretation. The only solid foundation to be found is truth, and the only place you find truth in the dreamstate is nowhere.

There's really nothing left for me to do but play with Maya—the goddess of illusion, not the dog—which, she is quick to remind me, is all I've ever really done. All my clever idea-play has kept me amused, but I'm still sitting on a dead planet in the middle of nowhere and Maya—take your pick—is my only friend. I'm not unique in this regard; it's the same for everyone, the only difference is whether or not you know it.

There's nowhere to go because there's nowhere to be. Evolution is just a name we give to the illusion of motion, and wisdom is just a mirage. Despite all the talk of journeys and progress and growth, no one has ever moved an inch. You appear in the amusement park and you play the games and ride the rides and when it's over you go out the way you came in. There was never any chance of making a difference because *you* were as much an illusion as the rest of it.

Wherever we turn in this house of mirrors, it all reflects back so bendy and distorted that no matter how hard we focus or how well we think, we can never make it make sense. We assume the mirrors are reflecting something real and if we could just get steady, get right in our own heads, the images would stop wobbling around and snap into focus. But we can never see things as they actually are because nothing is as it actually is, and no amount of steely thought or silent mind can make something of nothing.

If the doors of perception were cleansed, everything
would appear to man as it is, Infinite. For man has closed

himself up, till he sees all things through narrow chinks of
his cavern.

-William Blake

Blake's doors of perception might best be understood as
the distorting layers of ego. The only way to see clearly is not
to cleanse them but to remove them. Then, once they're gone,
you get to behold the infinite, but so what? Great, it's infinite.
Duh! So you turn to go back into the amusing albeit unreal
reality you left so you could behold the infinitely unamusing
infinite and, surprise, you can't go home again. You traded
the dream of something for the truth of nothing, and now
you want your something back. But you can't have it.

It's not that you want to be under a spell again, you just
don't want to be bored. Maybe in *The Matrix* you can be
reinserted and have your memory of the truth wiped clean,
but short of a serious head injury, you can't do that here. You
stepped out of the theater, the amusement park, the dream,
the video game, and discovered that it's boring out there and
that boredom is the one true enemy, so you sneak back in
and try to reinhabit the dreamscape you once called reality.
It's not easy, but if you can fool yourself even a little, doublethink your way back into a light doze, you can be a little
less bored. You can participate to some small degree, have a
purpose to some small degree, be amused by drama to some
small degree. You have to keep moving, though, or at least
create the illusion of motion, because as soon as you slow
down and allow your eyes to focus on any given point for
any length of time, the whole thing starts to dissolve. Never
focus, that's the key. Just let your vision go soft and let the

dreamworld shimmer back into place.

Ironically, the illusion you strove to escape is now something you must learn to nurture and cultivate. It's exceedingly delicate, like sleeping when you're not tired. You lay there and close your eyes and try to let the dreams come, but you can't fall asleep again. Any thought, any sound, any disturbance, and you snap back into alertness and the delicate dreamworld vanishes as if it was never really there.

✿

Let's take a few minutes to prove once and for all that there's no such thing as God. (Just kidding, it won't take that long.)

I Am is the only thing any sentient being can know. There is no higher someone that somehow knows something you don't because it's not possible for any conscious entity to know more than I Am. No one can have any other knowledge because there's no other knowledge to be had. That's not a *you* limitation or a *human* limitation, that's a *consciousness* limitation. No one can know more than I Am, so what does that make God? Can there be a supreme being who doesn't know any more than you or me? A supreme being who is entirely belief-based? In other words, delusional? Of course not. Once we've ruled out the possibility of knowledge, we've ruled out the possibility of God. Just that simple. No God, no higher beings, no all-knowers or insiders of any kind. But don't waste a tear on God or Allah or whoever else you thought was up there, the truth is much better than the fairytales.

Beyond I Am, it's all belief. There is nothing to know

because there is only consciousness, and that thou art. Ignorance is not a matter of what we don't know, but what we do know that's not true. In the dreamstate, false knowledge is everything and true knowledge is *Sentio, ergo sum*. I am aware, therefore I am. I-Am/Consciousness.

So, with one diamond bullet, we have killed God, gods, science, philosophy, religion, and any and all other claimants to knowledge, and we didn't use belief to do it, we *proved* it. Not bad for a couple of paragraphs. I-Am/Consciousness is the weapon that destroys the universe.

Pashupatastra!

✿

So now, having established that no one can possibly know anything more than I-Am/Consciousness, that no other knowledge is possible, that everything else is just belief and no belief is true, we can go back to our earlier statement that all of creation boils down to two things, one of which doesn't exist. Awareness is truth and appearance is belief. Instead of awareness and appearance, we can say dreamer and dream, beholder and beheld, or yin and yang. There's plenty to be said about appearance, but the only thing you can say with certainty is that it's not true, just as you can say with certainty that untruth does not exist. Consciousness is true and truth exists. The content of consciousness is not true and untruth does not exist.

Although it's not true and doesn't exist, appearance is absolutely necessary. Without appearance, there can be no awareness, but there *is* awareness so there must be appearance. Without anything to be aware of, awareness is not aware. Without anything to be aware of it, appearance does not appear. Yin and yang.

This begs a lot of which-came-first type questions, all of which are nullified by the fact that consciousness does not exist within time. There is no causality, no this-then-that, there is only *Is*. It's not very satisfying, but it's undeniable. We are the dreamer and what we call reality is the dream. That's as far as you get when you start digging because no matter where you dig in a dream, you just keep digging forever. I don't understand the dreamstate, but I do understand that it can't be understood. You can wake up *in* the dreamstate and you can wake up *from* the dreamstate, but you can't wake up *to* the dreamstate. There's nothing there to wake up to.

In order to explain the nature of reality, you would first have to determine that reality actually exists, which, actually, you can't. Yes, reality is obviously real, but the fact is that no one has ever proven that reality exists and no one ever will because no one can prove anything. There is no such thing as *ob*jective knowledge and the only *sub*jective knowledge is I-Am/Consciousness.

All supposed knowledge is really belief masquerading as knowledge, and the word for belief masquerading as knowledge is delusion. If everything you think you know is really just belief, and if belief itself is knowably false, then your entire reality can in no way be distinguished from a dream. There is no truth in the dreamstate because, in truth, there is no dreamstate.

That Poor Little Drop of Water

A conversation between protagonist Larry Darrell and W. Somerset Maugham, author as himself, from The Razor's Edge. *Larry begins.*

"ACCORDING TO THE VEDANTISTS, the self, which they call the atman and we call the soul, is distinct from the body and its senses, distinct from the mind and its intelligence; it is not part of the Absolute, for the Absolute, being infinite, can have no parts but the Absolute itself. It is uncreated; it has existed from eternity and when at last it has cast off the seven veils of ignorance will return to the infinitude from which it came. It is like a drop of water that has arisen from the sea, and in a shower has fallen into a puddle, then drifts into a brook, finds its way into a stream, after that into a river, passing through mountain gorges and wide plains, winding this way and that, obstructed by rocks and fallen trees, till at last it reaches the boundless seas from which it rose."

"But that poor little drop of water, when it has once more become one with the sea, has surely lost its individuality."

Larry grinned.

"You want to taste sugar, you don't want to become sugar. What is individuality but the expression of our egoism? Until the soul has shed the last trace of that, it cannot become one with the Absolute."

"You talk very familiarly of the Absolute, Larry, and it's an imposing word. What does it actually signify to you?"

"Reality. You can't say what it is; you can only say what it isn't. It's inexpressible. The Indians call it Brahman. It's not a person, it's not a thing, it's not a cause. It has no qualities. It transcends permanence and change; whole and part, finite and infinite. It is eternal because its completeness and perfection are unrelated to time. It is truth and freedom."

"Golly," I said to myself.

-W. Somerset Maugham

Alice in Dreamland

I'm not strange, weird, off, nor crazy,
my reality is just different from yours.

Lewis Carroll

"ARE THERE ANY LIONS OR TIGERS about here?" asked Alice timidly.

"It's only the Red King snoring," said Tweedledee.

"Come and look at him!" cried Tweedledum, and they each took one of Alice's hands, and led her up to where the Red King was sleeping.

"Isn't he a lovely sight?" said Tweedledum.

"The Red King is dreaming now," said Tweedledee, "and what do you think he's dreaming about?"

Alice said, "Nobody can guess that."

"Why, about you!" Tweedledum exclaimed, clapping his hands triumphantly. "And if he woke up this very instant, where do you think you'd be?"

"Where I am now, of course," said Alice.

"Not so!" Tweedledee retorted contemptuously. "You'd be nowhere. Why, you're only a sort of thing in his dream!"

"But the Red King is not dreaming *me*," protested an increasingly distraught Alice, "I am dreaming *him*. I am dreaming all of this! I am napping on the river bank as my sister reads a terribly dull book with no pictures or conversations…"

"Not so, not so," interrupted Tweedledum.

"That was maybe *that* time," corrected Tweedledee.

"Contrariwise, this is maybe *this* time," said Tweedledum.

"This time you are a pawn in the Red King's dream," said Tweedledee.

"And if you wake him, you'll go out—*bang!*—just like a candle!" said Tweedledum.

"No, no, no," cried a teary-eyed Alice, "if I wake myself, you'll all disappear!"

"But you're not sleeping this time," said Tweedledee.

"This time you passed through the looking-glass," remarked Tweedledum, "the question is, did you pass *downwardly* into your own dream?"

"Or *upwardly*," said Tweedledee, "into the dream of *you*?"

"It's a mystery, I'd say," said Tweedledum.

"If I'm only a sort of thing in his dream," protested Alice, "what are *you*, I should like to know?"

"Ditto," said Tweedledee.

"Ditto, ditto," cried Tweedledum.

They shouted so loud that Alice couldn't help saying, "Hush! You'll be waking him, I'm afraid, if you make so much noise."

"Well, it's no use *your* talking about waking him," said Tweedledee, "when you're only one of the things in his dream.

You know very well you're not real."

"I am real!" said Alice and began to cry.

"You won't make yourself a bit realer by crying," Tweedledum remarked. "There's nothing to cry about."

"If I wasn't real," Alice said, half-laughing through her tears, it all seemed so ridiculous, "I shouldn't be able to cry."

"I hope you don't suppose those are real tears?" Tweedledee interrupted in a tone of great contempt.

"I know they're talking nonsense," Alice thought to herself, "and it's foolish to cry about it."

"So," said Tweedledum in a voice that Alice found far too loud, "shall we give the sleeping king a kick?"

"Yes, let's do!" cried Tweedledee. "Let's see who disappears!"

"No! Please don't!" said Alice, suddenly much less certain as to who was dreaming and who was dreamt, and not at all eager to take a chance. Who, after all, wants to go out— *bang!*—just like a candle?

"If I were only a sort of thing in the Red King's dream," reasoned Alice laboriously, "I would not think I *was*, nor would I think I was *not*. However, I *do* think I'm not, therefore I most certainly *am* not!"

She wasn't absolutely sure of her logic, but hoped it might fool the Tweedles, which it did, but their confusion was brief.

"No way, no how," said Tweedledum.

"No points for twisty logic," cried Tweedledee.

"The question," explained Tweedledum, "is who is dreaming who?"

"Are you dreaming the Red King?" asked his brother.

"Or is the Red King dreaming you?"

"We can't all be dreaming each other!" said Tweedledee

"No," said his brother, "that would never do."

"Why must you speak in rhyme all the time?" demanded a nearly sobbing Alice, "it's not that I'm dense, but that nothing makes sense!"

"But there you are wrong," sang the boys in a song,
 "with that we just cannot agree!
Though it may not always *seem* to be,
 order presides over all that you see;
And as crazy as the game is played,
 the rules are the rules and must be obeyed!"

"A Pawn can't never move like a Knight,
 and the Red Side can't never play White.
Each piece has its limits, the board has its border,
 so you see what we mean, when we say that it seems,
Without limits and borders we'd live in disorder!"

"The King, though quite mighty, is weak on his own.
Any Pawn can be Queen, but no Queen can be Pawn.
No piece is endowed with a will that is free.
The rules are for all, even Kings must agree!"

"If it weren't for the rules, then where would we be?
Without law and order, there'd be no you and me!
You think it's a dream so anything goes,
But even dreams must have rules, and rules run the show!"

"Whoa," said Alice, "no shit."

And it was at this very moment that Alice decided that she would no longer be a slave to events, getting grown big and shrunk small and bibbled and bobbled about like a ribbon on the wind. From now on, she decided, come what may, whatever the cost, she would be the master of the dreamworld in which she found herself!

"Thank you," said Alice, "for showing me,
  What for so long I have longed to see.
  That I'm just a prisoner inside of a dream,
  And nothing here is as it seems."

So she drew a sword from a nearby tree
  And deftly beheaded Tweedle-Dee.
  And seeing that it was all in good fun,
  She promptly skewered Tweedle-Dum.

The Question of Intelligence

Things are entirely what they appear to
be and behind them, there is nothing.

Jean-Paul Sartre

H ERE'S A FUN QUESTION: Does intelligence exist? If so,
is it awareness or appearance? If appearance, then
intelligence does not exist in truth and therefore not at all. If
awareness, then it must be synonymous with consciousness,
not an attribute of it, meaning that infinite consciousness
and perfect intelligence are the same thing. Therefore, either
intelligence does *not* exist in truth, or it is synonymous with
consciousness.

This is where we hit the hard wall of truth and take a step
back, meaning that nothing we say from this point forward is
true, just playful speculation. We can do the best we can, but
we are now permanently consigned to the belief side of the
wall with the likes of science and religion. We can certainly
do better than them, but we still can't arrive at knowledge.

Unless maybe we can.

☼

Time out for a few introductions. Brahman is consciousnesses; the impersonal, featureless infinite. Maya is the creator of the dreamstate, and Atman is the aspect of Brahman that beholds Maya's creation. They are not entities, they are tools for understanding. On the truth side of the hard wall is Brahman. Maya and Atman are on the belief side.

Okay, time in.

☼

Let's begin by deciding what we mean by intelligence. Offhand, I'd say it was the power to manifest coherent appearance. Intelligence would thus constitute a closed-loop perpetual dream machine in which infinite consciousness (Brahman) creates appearance (as Maya) solely to entertain itself (as Atman). The coherent appearance thus rendered would certainly be devoid of substance and meaning, and may or may not be amusing to behold (the dreamstate).

Appearance is illusion. Belief that appearance is real is *delusion*. Just because the Mayan aspect of Brahman can create illusion doesn't mean that the Atmanic aspect of Brahman can be deceived by it, and without that, there is no solution to the problem of Brahmanic boredom. We'll come back to this later, but for now I'll just say that the solution to the problem is you.

☼

If we say that the dreamstate exists, then we are necessarily saying that intelligence exists. The problem, alas, is that we can't say that the dreamstate exists, so we can't use it to say anything else. Nor can we say that intelligence is an *attribute* of consciousness because it's definitively impossible for the infinite to have attributes.

But there's a loophole. *Perfect* intelligence wouldn't be an attribute *of* consciousness, it would be synonymous *with* it, so we'd be saying that perfect intelligence and infinite consciousness are two ways of saying the same thing. I'm not sure we *can* say that, but we might have to.

The question of intelligence is obviously not a simple one. Deductive reasoning tells us as a certainty that consciousness is true, that the universe of appearances is *un*true, and that untruth does not exist. However, to say that infinite consciousness and perfect intelligence are synonymous is an example of *in*ductive reasoning. It looks good, it fits the observable data, there's no compelling alternative, and it sounds right, but it's not certain and can't be made certain.

✿

The word *coherent* in coherent appearance refers to the perfect organizational structure of appearance which we see in all things. If we don't see this perfection, it's not because it's not there or not perfect, but because we're looking through the lens of ego. Harken back to the William Blake quote: If we could see without the distorting influence of ego, everything would appear as it is, perfect.

The doors of my perception are cleansed, so I see all that is and nothing that's not. Do I see intelligence? No. Well, technically no, but really, yes. But still, no. And yes. I see the dreamstate, but I also see through it. As with a dream, I see it, but I see that it's not really there. Does dismissing a thing as mere appearance also dismiss the creative intelligence underlying that appearance? Maybe not, but it does make it hard to prove. You can see how this gets a little tricky. Maybe this is why Descartes chose *cogito* instead of *sentio*; he wanted to just tiptoe around this whole headachy conversation.

☼

I *observe* intelligence, but there's no airtight Cartesian maxim that *proves* intelligence. I can say, "I am aware, therefore awareness exists," but I can't say, "I am intelligent, therefore intelligence exists." I don't know I'm intelligent any more than I know I'm a dolphin having a past-life regression. The world is simply an appearance to which I affably subscribe. When on Earth, do as the Earthlings do.

Because we can't know that we think, Descartes should have said *sentio, ergo sum;* I am aware, therefore I am. *Cogito* is just another appearance about which I can be deceived, *Sentio* is not. The distinction between "I think" and "I am aware" is right where we're stuck at the moment. I know I'm aware, but I only believe that I think.

We could almost say that intelligence *must* exist to be observed, so observing it proves it exists. Almost, but not quite. Delusion lies prior to perception, so nothing has to exist in order to be observed. We can almost say that intelligence must be an exception, but again, not quite.

Which brings us to the real question. Even though we know the content of the dream is *not* true, can we say that the intelligence of the dream *is* true? Is it possible that *what*

Brahman dreams is untrue, but it's true that Brahman dreams? That doesn't sound so bad, but no, we can't say it for sure. Even the structural elements of the dreamstate are still made of wisps of dreamstuff, and you can't make something from nothing.

✿

So, those are the pieces of the ultimate mystery. The only part we can be sure of is infinite consciousness. All the rest is just our inherently doomed effort to account for the existence of appearance. The bottom-line solution to the mystery of appearance is that it doesn't exist, so there is no mystery. That's really where it ends. What we're doing here is ignoring that hard truth so we can try to solve the mystery of the dreamstate from within the dreamstate, which we can't, and which is why we have to switch from knowledge to belief at this point.

✿

Fun fact: We have now traveled beyond all belief systems to the outermost reaches of philosophy, and all we needed to get here was a little respect for the cogito.

✿

Why did Iago go all psycho on Desdemona and Othello? Because Shakespeare said so, that's why. It's a dream within a dream, and as hard as we might try to make sense of it, there's no sense to be made. We can try to figure out what Josef K. is accused of in *The Trial*, but we can never *know* because there are no facts to work with. There was no Josef

K., there was no crime, and there was no trial. It's all just something from Kafka's imagination. Some things may be true within the context of a story, but the story itself is a false context. This applies to the story we call reality; there are no facts to work with, it's all just imagination, including the appearance of coherence; intelligence. We can't hold the dreamstate to account, and we can't summon the author and demand a straight answer because the author is just another character in the story.

Which naturally brings us to our next question. Does Superman have bulletproof balls? The answer, of course, is yes. Why? Because he's Superman, that's why. You can heat his balls in a forge and smash them on an anvil, submerge them in ice, make them listen to country music, teabag a school of piranha, punch them like a speedbag, have the waiter grate them over your Angel Hair Pasta with Garlic Shrimp and Broccoli, let a puppy play with them with those sharp little teeth, roll up a damp towel and snap 'em a few good ones, even make a set of voodoo balls and stick them with red-hot pins, and Superman will just look at you like you're wasting his time. Why? Because in the Superman universe, Super*man* has super *balls*. We can even apply a paradox; If he's so super he should be able to crush his own balls like grapes, but if his balls can be crushed like grapes, then he can't be all that super. I call it *The Paradox of Superman's Balls*. Suck it, Xeno. Anyway, the point is, uh… oh nuts, I forgot the point. That's too bad, too, because I was just about to blow this whole question-of-intelligence thing wide open. Curse you, balls of steel!

✿

Now cease your infantile giggling and ponder yonder yin-yang. The white part is awareness, the black part is appearance, the circle is artificial finiteness, and the infinite white field on which the symbol sits is consciousness. Black is Maya, the white in the circle is Atman, and the white of the infinite field is Brahman. Taken together, the yin-yang is the symbol of you as you wrongly believe yourself to be, *self*, and the infinite white field is you as you really are, *no-self*.

That's the totality of dreamstate being in a single symbol, so where in the symbol do we place intelligence? If intelligence is in the black, it's a nonexistent appearance. If intelligence is in the white part of the circle, it's an attribute of consciousness, which is without attributes. The only place it can be is in the infinite field of consciousness, and the only way it can be there is if intelligence and consciousness are the same thing.

So, if intelligence exists in truth, it must exist *as* consciousness, and if so, then it must be true that perfect intelligence and infinite consciousness are the same thing rather than either being a feature of the other. But we can only say all *that* if we can say that intelligence exists at *all*, which we can't. We can only say that it really, really *seems* to exist.

✿

If the three options for the intelligence of consciousness are zero, imperfect and perfect, then through the process of elimination, perfect is looking pretty good. Can consciousness be devoid of intelligence? I would say no, and *im*perfect intelligence can certainly be ruled out, so here we are back to saying that perfect intelligence is synonymous with infinite consciousness. We almost can't say that intelligence does *not* exist, and we can't say it exists as an attribute of consciousness, so we go for the loophole and say perfect intelligence is synonymous with infinite consciousness and hope that no one calls bullshit, which it is. So close, yet so far.

And that's where the line is drawn. We can *know* that consciousness is all, but we can only *speculate* that intelligence exists, so we can only *believe* that consciousness and intelligence are the same thing.

So, does intelligence exist? We can't say for sure that it does or it doesn't, so I'm invoking artistic license for the purposes of this book and saying yes; infinite consciousness and perfect intelligence are two ways of saying the same thing.

Perfect intelligence is true. *(wink)*

Pillows of Illusion

All is riddle, and the key to a riddle is another riddle. There are as many pillows of illusion as flakes in a snowstorm. We wake from one dream into another dream. The toys, to be sure, are various, and are graduated in refinement to the quality of the dupe. The intellectual man requires a fine bait; the sots are easily amused. But everybody is drugged with his own frenzy, and the pageant marches at all hours, with music and banner and badge.

R.W. Emerson

IT'S AROUND MIDNIGHT. I'm semi-reclined on the couch in front of the fire wrapped in a wool blanket drinking wine with my feet tucked under the dog while wondering if my thoughts are clear and if I'm getting them down on the page correctly which, judging from this dopey paragraph, I'm not.

Right now my concern is whether the stuff I'm writing is too much or not enough. It doesn't matter, it'll get cleaned up or thrown out later. The real thing I'm worried about is the girl sleeping on my recliner and snoring like a cartoon villain. It's like she's under some fairy tale curse; pretty young lady by day, scary growly-monster by night. Someone should get in there with some tough love and a scalpel and modify her septum. I'm wondering if there's anything in the junk drawer that's pretty sharp and not too rusty when she switches from guttural snarling to human speech.

"Oh," she says, stretching, "I must have dozed off. Was I snoring?"

"Just little princess chirps."

"My roommate says I snore like a lumberjack."

"I take exception to that. All the lumberjacks I've known have been very dainty sleepers. I remember one, Sweet-Snore Pierre we called him. He was such a lovely snorer that people would gather…"

"Is there coffee?"

"If you make it."

"Are you working on the screenplay?"

"Not visibly."

"Are you going to?"

"I already am."

"But not visibly?"

"No."

"Okay. I have to go."

"Okay."

✿

The screenplay is the project Maggie wants us to work on together. I don't think it will go anywhere, but I never think any writing project will go anywhere until it does, so I try not to rule things out impulsively.

She wants to write a screenplay and submit it at one of her schools because the selected submission will be funded and equipped, so if we write something that wins, she gets to make her first movie. Her suggestion was a rip-off of *My Dinner With Andre*, which makes a lot of sense given limited resources; one set, two principals, a few extras, no complicated chase scenes or expensive CGI. The thing, though, is that you need the content, you need someone who can ramble on for ninety minutes without inducing catatonia. The jury is very much out as to whether Andre managed it, so how does Maggie plan to pull it off? Enter, me. I'm her ace. Instead of Andre, it's dinner with Jed.

I said no for the first few weeks but the idea kind of seeped into my brain as a possibly viable message platform, depending on the message. I started thinking that regardless of whether or not it got made, it might be fun to write. By the time I had thought it through that far, I had realized we'd need to have Lisa on board as well because she would have to be the Wally to my Andre, and she might not be too thrilled about that.

✵

If we measure a conspiracy nut by the size of his theory, then I am the biggest crackpot of all. I believe reality isn't real, there's no such thing as self, and the universe is just an elaborate hoax perpetrated by a shadowy puppetmaster code-named Maya.

A conspiracy theory must have three parts; narrative, theory, and truth. The narrative is the story we're asked to believe, and the theory is the story we suspect. The truth is the invisible hub around which the conspiracy constellation rotates, but is otherwise surprisingly irrelevant.

Stories, such as movies, plays, television shows and novels, are narratives to which we eagerly subject ourselves and by which we are willingly deceived. A magic act is a kind of conspiracy in which we playfully withhold our belief by trying to see through the narrative, and consider the performance a success if we can't. Politics is conspiracy taken a step further, preying upon hope and fear to make us suspend disbelief despite common sense and historical precedent. Advertising is more of the same; the art and science of monetizing fear. Religion and spirituality are similar to politics insofar as the sauce of our hunger compensates for an unswallowable narrative. Science is similar to religion and spirituality in that proponents actually subscribe to the narrative. Viewed on a spectrum, we might see fairytales, mythology and religion on the far left and mathematics on the far right, with all the others sprinkled in-between, but the one thing they all have in common is that none of them are true.

So when we talk about conspiracy, the question is not if we are on occasion deceived, but if there is any tiny corner of our lives that is not a lie, and the answer is no. It's not that we encounter some small falsehoods within the larger truth, but that reality itself is a false narrative and self itself is a lie. Life is but a dream, and there is no truth in dreams.

☼

If you want to find the truth within, the inner black hole is where you must go. Not to it, but through it. It's like an internal toilet of which we are so profoundly ashamed that we can't acknowledge its existence, even to ourselves. We live our life swirling around the bowl, caught between the centrifugal lifeforce holding us up and gravitational death-force pulling us down. Ego has many tools to maintain the balance of these forces, while other facets of ego threaten their disruption.

This inner toilet out-Borgs the Borg in its unyielding inevitability: Resistance *is* futile and you *will* be assimilated. The collective awaits and will not be denied, and no one can save you because you never actually *de*-assimilated. Your pathetic sense of individuality is just a lonely little dreamcloud in the universal mind.

Try as we might and wish as we will, the inner commode can't be plugged or clogged, so we distract ourselves from it when we can and convince ourselves it's a gateway to something better when we can't. Sometimes, we're told, the system backs up and someone returns from beyond the trap to assure us that our most desperate hopes are true; that the outflow from this toilet is the inflow to a better one.

Our quality of life experience depends on our ability to remain blissfully ignorant of the painfully obvious truth that, with every passing moment, we are swirling into the void. It's not enough to resist this alarming downtrend, we must maintain an active ignorance of it while also remaining unaware that we are doing so: Doublethink. This is quite a challenge, but ego is a remarkable feat of spiritual plumbing designed for this exact purpose.

It's not pleasant to think of Maya's Palace of Illusion as a porcelain shitter or of the journey of life as a spinning into oblivion. It's much more pleasant to deny and delay as long as lifeforce allows. Most people probably only allow themselves to glimpse the inevitable destination a few times in life, and quickly turn away. For the purpose of a happy life it's better to never look down, never acknowledge your situation, even if you have to go soft in the head to do it. Being a bit more stupid or crazy than comes natural is a small price to pay to maintain blissful ignorance. That dark hole at the bottom of the bowl is the exit from the fiction of you, so if you think of it as the gateway to truth, then the price of the sought is the end of the seeker and the prime directive of the spiritual search is not *Know* Thyself but *Flush* Thyself.

Map of the Dreamstate

A point is reached where the self is so completely aligned
with the still-point that it can no longer be moved, even
in its first movements, from this center. It can no longer
be tested by any force or trial, nor moved by the winds of
change, and at this point the self has obviously outworn
its function; it is no longer needed or useful, and life can
go on without it.

Bernadette Roberts

WELCOME TO THIS CHAPTER. Here we will look at the map of the dreamstate in which we use the black hole in outer space as a metaphor for the black hole in inner space. I enjoy conspiracy theories, so while we're talking about black holes it seems appropriate to take a look at their chief spokesman.

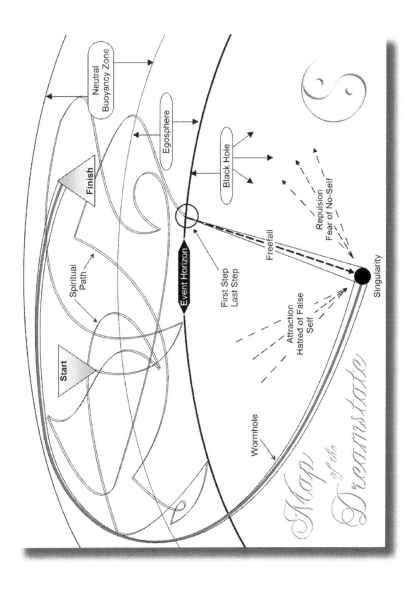

Map of the Dreamstate

As of this writing, we are given to believe that Professor Stephen Hawking still rolls the Earth. We accept this fact because, you know, why not? But if we stop and think about it for a minute, it seems pretty possible that the real guy died in the mid-eighties and some nefarious "they" stuck in a ringer for some nefarious reason. This semi-plausible theory is much more amusing than the narrative that it's really him, which brings me to the moral of the story which is that, in the dreamstate, it's better to be amused than correct.

And now I use this little paragraph to segue back into this chapter's topic, which is not about black holes in outer space, but the one at the center of you.

✿

Behold, the Map of the Dreamstate.

THE SPIRITUAL PATH

That squiggly double-line on the map is your spiritual path, which is basically just your life. You start where you start and you go where you go. It doesn't matter where you start or where you go or what you believe or what you do, all that matters is if you cross the event horizon. Until that line is crossed, regardless of any other consideration, you are just a character on a stage playing a role, and any role, in the context of awakening, is the same as any other. So, you start fresh with every step and you either move toward singularity or you continue to squiggle around.

Your spiritual path crosses in and out of the egosphere as your spiritual intensity waxes and wanes. A sound asleep person might squiggle around near their starting point for their entire life, while someone struggling to awaken might make an epiphany-driven dash for the black hole singularity without much squiggling at all. Neither of those, however, would have much reason to be reading this book, so you're probably more like the line on the map.

Twice on the map we see the spiritual path nearly crossing the event horizon before turning back. There are very impressive egoic agencies at work to keep us from strolling off this cliff. When you get yourself in a frenzy of truth-longing due to some inspiration or insight, these protective agencies come online and redirect your self-destructive energy so it gets channeled back to safety. Then you are guided back to equilibrium, wad shot, until the next time you get yourself all revved up. This is ego in its self-preservation mode, and it is, in my view, the second coolest thing in the dreamstate after dogs.

Singularity

If returning is the motion of the Tao, then it is to the singularity you return and, having returned, realize you never really left and just dreamed the whole thing. The singularity is the truth of you; Brahman, the I-Am/Consciousness truth-center of your I-universe. At the exact center of the dreamstate of that-thou-aren't is the singularity of infinite consciousness, and that thou art.

Attraction & Repulsion

Hatred and fear are the push-me pull-you forces of dreamstate harmony. Hatred of false self pulls us toward singularity and fear of no-self pushes us away. Cousin to the fear of no-self would be fear of death, and any state of passion that makes you heedless of that fear would be a cousin to the hatred of false self. We don't feel crushed or torn by these forces when they are in balance, but when they go out of whack we experience them quite distinctly.

The only energy at your disposal is emotion, so if you want to make the journey toward singularity you must harness and focus your emotional energy. This can happen intentionally or spontaneously, meaning you can do a swan dive off the event horizon or accidentally saunter off, but either way, the result is a shift from a relatively stable experience of the neutral buoyancy zone to a gravity-powered collision course with truth.

The Neutral Buoyancy Zone

The neutral buoyancy zone is the state of spiritual equilibrium in which most people live out their lives. Neutral buoyancy is the sub-lucid condition in which the opposing forces of fear and hate are in balance. It's like being in a hot air balloon that has enough oomph to get off the ground, but not to escape the atmosphere. As long as lifeforce energy provides fuel, it can resist deathforce gravity and maintain altitude.

These forces that hold us in spiritual equilibrium are not evil or malicious and there's no demonic agency conspiring against us, it's just a regulating process that allows us to play our roles without realizing we're just buffoons in a farce, which would kind of spoil the effect. The idea that ego is bad and spiritual growth is good is just one of many motivational carrots for us to chase around the stage.

The Egosphere

The warning track around the event horizon is what scientists call the ergosphere, but egosphere works better for us.

There are many safety nets in the egosphere which will lure you in and gently ensnare you. They appear to offer what you seek, but will actually curtail your inward journey and turn it safely out. For instance, you might find yourself building up a head of steam, like it's time to really buckle down and make a serious effort, so you get a book about waking up and the book is pretty good so you get another one, and the next thing you know, spiritual books have satisfied your desire for spiritual progress and the danger of actual change has been averted. *(Does that make me an agent of delusion? You'd be wise to wonder.)*

As shown on the map, your spiritual path might bring you in and out of the egosphere many times. You might make a series of approaches and retreats, or you might find a new comfort zone somewhere closer to the event horizon. It might seem like the closer to the event horizon you are, the more awake you are, but paradigm shifts don't happen in degrees. Closer to the event horizon is not more awake, it's just less comfortable.

Event Horizon

The most important thing to know about the event horizon is that you never know where it is until you cross it, and then it's too late.

The last step of the flesh marks the first step of the spirit, where it will also be the last. It's just one step like any other, but now it's the last step because, unlike any other, this one takes you across the event horizon and you will never experience the illusion of firm footing again. Like Neo being unplugged from the Matrix and flushed out of the system, there's no going back. It's scary to open your eyes when you've spent your life not knowing they were closed. The first thing you see is that your entire life has been a fiction and now it's over. Your eyes hurt because you've never used them before, and you're starting to wish you chose the blue pill.

FREEFALL

Crossing the event horizon is what I have called the First Step, which is also the last step. In an outer-space black hole, the event horizon marks the beginning point of a gravitational pull so strong that not even light can escape. In the inner-space black hole, it also marks an absolute point of no return. Once the line is crossed, a paradigm shift has occurred and one dies from the old and is reborn into a new reality.

How long the period of freefall lasts depends on various factors, but the only one you might be able to control is your own resistance to the process. Resistance is not only futile, it's painful.

Crossing the event horizon can seem like a psychotic break, especially to the outside observers you are leaving behind. The dreamstate bubble pops and the illusion of firm footing is replaced by the reality of freefall. The sense of falling comes from the shredding and ripping away of ego. When that part's over, the sensation of motion is replaced by a sense of floating detachment, and that's how it stays.

WORMHOLE

When the last shred of ego is ripped away, singularity is

achieved and *whoosh!*, you shoot through the wormhole pipeline back to where you started. Now you're sane and everyone else is unbelievably nuts, so have fun with that. But first, you have to go through all sorts of learning and acclimating which corresponds to the processes of childhood growth and development you're already familiar with.

✿

Once you achieve singularity, or, in other words, once you have completed the severing of emotional attachments culminating in the killing of the Buddha by whatever name you know him, or, in still other words, once you unstrap your own version of a rat cage mask and crawl out of room 101, then you will understand what the wormhole is because you will find yourself right back in the dreamstate where you started, only now you're *in* the dream but not *of* the dream.

Now you will understand for yourself the whole mountain, not-a-mountain, mountain-again thing. Now you will be awake in the dreamstate which, really, if you think about it, is a pretty stupid place to be awake.

Regardless of how profound or complex ego makes it seem, that's all the spiritual journey really is. Cross the event horizon or don't, take the First Step or don't, there's nothing else to it. What is enlightenment? What is the Integrated State? The answer is not found in the words of the wise or the depths of the human heart, it's found in the black hole, and the event horizon is effectively the border between paradigms. The spiritual journey may not be easy, but it's definitely simple.

The Magic Lantern

"I quite agree with you," said the Duchess; "and the moral
of that is—'Be what you would seem to be'—or if you'd
like it put more simply—'Never imagine yourself not to be
otherwise than what it might appear to others that what
you were or might have been was not otherwise than
what you had been would have appeared to them to be
otherwise.'"

Lewis Carroll

ALICE STOOD WITH THE HATTER and the Dormouse and
the March Hare in the royal court where the Queen, the
Duchess, and all the Queen's subjects were in attendance.

"Where am I?" wondered Alice, not for the first time of
late.

"If it's *now*," said the Hatter, "then this must be *here*."

"I'm becoming very tired of *here* and *now*," complained
Alice. "I should very much like to be *there* and *then* for a
change."

"It was *then* yesterday," said the Hatter, "and you will be *there* tomorrow, but today you are *here* and here it is *now*."

"But what about when I woke up this morning? I seem to recall that I was *there* then and it was *then* there."

"Yes and no," said the Hatter. "*Now* it was then, but *then* it was *now*."

"And it was *here* when you were *there*," said the Dormouse, "but when you were *there* it was *here*."

"No, no," corrected the March Hare, "you mean it was *here* when she was *there*, but now that she's *here* it is *there*."

"That's what I said," the Dormouse said.

"I guess I can't argue with that," guessed Alice, "but I'm starting to think that I'm *always* here and it's *always* now, which would mean nothing ever changes and I must be frightfully bored!"

"And the moral of that," said the Duchess, "is that it's always better to be *some*where than *any*where, but *any*where is better than *no*where!"

"No," said Alice, "I don't think that's the moral at all."

"Right you are!" cried the Duchess.

The Queen had been listening to every word Alice said and felt she could sort out the whole matter in four little words.

"Off with her head!" cried the Queen.

"No!" cried the Hatter.

"No!" cried the Dormouse.

"No!" cried the March Hare.

"Yes!" cried Alice. *"Off with my head!"*

Now the whole court froze in silence and stared mutely at Alice.

"Take it," she demanded. "Silly bulbous thing, nothing but

trouble!" And although Alice was surprised to hear herself saying such a mad and scary thing, she felt she might finally be nearing the bottom of a hole she'd been plummeting down since way back at the start of her adventure.

"All my troubles seem to start with my head," she said to the assembled court. "Cut it off, I say, and we'll see what we see."

"But how will you see *anything*," asked the Dormouse, "if you don't have a head?"

"Off with my body!" amended Alice, "I will keep my head and you may chop my body off. The Cheshire Cat has only a head and he seems *quite* pleased."

(At this point, the Hatter whispered into Alice's ear that the Cheshire Cat did indeed have a complete body and that if she wished to have her head removed it should not be on the pretty improbable and probably impossible notion that bodies and heads could get along without each other.)

"Whatever I do," said Alice, "wherever I go, I am always stuck inside this knobby melon, always looking out but never seeing in. Why," she cogitated without quite knowing how, "I shouldn't wonder if it weren't some kind of magic-lantern projector and the entire world goes *out* through my head instead of coming *in*. I don't *really* know any different, do I?"

Alice was very satisfied with *that* thought and was just about to have *another* when it occurred to her that she wasn't quite done with the first one yet.

"Let's put it to the test," she said, and proceeded to confirm her suspicions by using the power of her mind to turn the entire court and all its inhabitants completely upside-down.

"*A-ha!*" she cried. "Just as I thought! Through a simple application of the mental arts, I have rearranged the laws of gravity and suspended all of you from the ceiling!"

"But my *dear*," said the Queen delicately, "you have simply turned *yourself* upside down. *We* are all just as we *were.*"

Alice was not flustered by so paltry a rebuttal.

"Naturally, *you* would say that," re-rebutted Alice, "but I can hardly accept the opinion of an upside-*down* person on the question of rightside-*upness*, now can I? All that matters to *me*, it seems to me, is how it seems to *me*. Why should I care how it seems to *you?* If I cared how it seemed to *you*, why, I would *be* you, and then who would *you* be? And who would be *me?*"

But now the blood was rushing to Alice's head, possibly, she surmised, from abuse of power, so she righted the room and curtsied to silent applause.

"And the moral of the story," bellowed the Duchess, "is that *gravity* is in the *eye* of the *beholder!*"

"No," said Alice, "I don't think it is."

"No, no, you're *quite* right," agreed the Duchess, "and the moral of *that* is, the moral of the story is whatever you *think* it is!"

"Perhaps not everything *has* a moral," suggested Alice.

"Right you are!" cried the Duchess. "And the moral of *that* is, there is *no* moral to *anything!*"

"Oh, bother," said Pooh, "I've wandered into the wrong universe again."

The Problem of Perfection

I am not quite sure whether I am dreaming or remembering, whether I have lived my life or dreamed it. Just as dreams do, memory makes me profoundly aware of the unreality, the evanescence of the world, a fleeting image in the moving water.

Eugene Ionesco

S AY, HYPOTHETICALLY, THAT YOU WERE watching the universe on TV. You have infinite channels. You can watch anything you want, but ego has not been invented yet so you only have nature channels. You have a universal remote and you are the master of all you survey. You can watch any*thing* any*where* any*when,* so what do you choose? Water flowing? Grass growing? Planets spinning? Gazelles eating and being eaten? Schools of fish darting about? How about rivers shaping rocks or wind shaping mountains? How about the birth of oceans or stars or giraffes? Anything you want, anything you can think of.

You see where this is going, right? You don't really have *infinite* channels, you only have *one* channel, and it's so hellishly boring that you're going out of your mind, not after a few billion years but around the thirty-minute mark. That's how long it would take you to start going seriously bonkers. And you can't turn off Universe-TV and read a book or go out and play because UTV is all there is. There is only appearance and the entire spectrum of appearance is equally boring. You have the whole universe to amuse you, but the universe is simply not amusing, which is a problem because amusing you is all it exists to do. It serves no other purpose. Awareness needs to be aware of something; something *not* boring. There is no awareness without appearance, but not just any appearance will do. Would it do for you? How long could you watch an unnarrated, unedited, unscored nature channel? You'd turn into a drooling idiot before lunch. Boredom is the problem the universe exists to solve, but the perfect clockwork universe isn't solving it, and there's no possibility of imperfection to spice things up.

Keep in mind as we sort this out that the universe does not actually exist. The universe is rendered into existence without actually existing the same way a dream is rendered into existence without actually existing. Nothing actually exists except infinite, featureless consciousness: Brahman.

So, that's the situation. The universe of appearance is boring, and being boring is not the minor issue it may seem. For Brahman, it's actually the most serious possible issue. It's a problem that cannot be tolerated. The universe, such it is, exists, such as it does, as an antidote to boredom, but it *is* boring and can't *not* be boring. The perfect clockwork universe, which exists solely to amuse, doesn't and can't.

✿

While we're in the neighborhood, let's address the sole beholder issue. How many Atmans are there? As to the number of beholders *of* the dreamstate *in* the dreamstate, the correct answer would constitute knowledge and is, therefore, unknowable and only a matter for light conjecture. The three possibilities of how many discrete sentient entities (like yourself) exist are one; one (just you, which seems unlikely), two; a bunch of us (as it appears), and three; infinite (why not?).

As to three, infinite Atmans, I don't like treating infinity as a number, but since we're talking about the actual infinite, there's no practical limit so we can make an exception. Three is also tempting if you want to explain the dreamstate as a fractal hologram or a holographic fractal or some other wonderfully clever but unsupportable hypothesis.

Options two and three make sense and one doesn't. We can't rule it out, but the only reason to believe I am the only sentient entity, the sole beholder, is that it's theoretically possible and therefore of the same theoretical probability as two and three. Keep in mind, there are no answers to any of this. No one *knows* because there is no such thing as objective knowledge. So, as we see here, possibilities cannot be converted to probabilities. I might like two more than one or three, but they're all equally possible.

Ultimately, of course, the answer is simple. Brahman is the sole beholder.

✿

So now, back to this issue of the universe being boring. That doesn't sound like a real problem, but it really is. See for yourself. You have as much right and authority to weigh in on this as anyone. If you're at all like me, you have a very low tolerance for boredom. We're all like kids squirming in the backseat on a long, hot drive. Maybe there's some remote Himalayan cult of boredom-loving people who stare at dirt all day, but in general, we are not designed for watching paint dry or grass grow. Boredom sucks. I'm not just saying that as a character but also as Atman, and as for Atman, so for Brahman. A boring appearance is just as bad as no appearance at all.

Brahman has no use for Maya if she's just going to sit there and read the phone book, but what choice does Maya have? She has no scripts or stageplays to perform, no poems to read or songs to sing, no drama or conflict to enact. All she can do is keep tick-tocking along, and the result is a perfectly boring clockwork universe which isn't addressing the one problem it was conjured to solve.

The perfection of creation may not be apparent from the egoic point of view, which brings us back to our modified Blake quote again; when perception is de-egofied, everything appears as it is, perfect. If the perfection of creation is not apparent from your point of view, that makes sense because your false point of view is the whole point of you. It is, in fact, what you are; an inaccurate point of view.

✿

You might think that Maya, with perfect intelligence at her command, would be able to shake it up a bit, throw in a few curves, sprinkle a little chaos here and there, come up with her own drama and conflict, but that's not possible. The shortcoming of perfection is that it's perfect, and for this reason, the universe can't be exciting or surprising. It cannot amuse. It can only sit there, ticking along like a Swiss watch; always perfect, no surprises. You can say all sorts of wonderful things about a Swiss watch, but you can't say it's amusing to look at for very long.

What you might prefer to look at is not a Swiss watch, but a Swiss cuckoo clock, so that, as you sit and stare and your mind turns to sludge, some crazy asshole bird suddenly pops out and makes a bunch of noise and scares the shit out of you. Then it withdraws and you lapse back into light clock-watching catatonia until eventually—*bam!*—there goes that crazy asshole bird again. It's not great, but it's better than watching a watch. Something is actually happening. Now we have drama, suspense, anxiety, emotional content, and *that's* entertainment.

✷

What we're doing here is answering the biggest question. However you phrase it—What is the meaning of life? What is my purpose? What's the point?, Who am I? What is true? etc—we are, right now, looking at the one and only explanation for everything. We can further clarify the issue by reducing it to the two things we know exist, one of which doesn't; awareness and appearance. Whenever we ask the biggest questions, we are asking about appearance. Why does appearance appear? The only possible answer, obviously, is that appearance appears for the sake of awareness. What else? And why does awareness need appearance? Because if it's not aware of something, then it's not aware at all, but there's nothing to be aware of, so something must be fabricated.

It's kind of a weird and unsatisfying explanation, not what we might have hoped or expected, but the elements of the equation are certain and only add up one way. All belief aside, the timespace, energymatter, dualistic, causalistic universe is obviously just spectacle for the sake of spectacle. The dreamstate is to Brahman as movies, television, stories, plays, books, and video games are to us. There is no higher meaning, no redeeming value; no one is going anywhere and nothing matters. However you run the numbers, it always adds up to one. This is available to direct and certain knowing, so if you do the math, this is what you get.

✿

A simplified way to say it is that One exists. One is bordered by Two and Zero, neither of which exist, but both of which exert an influence on One. One is repelled by Zero and drawn toward Two. Zero is empty and boring, Two is empty but amusing. One cannot *become* Two, but it can, through perfect, infinite intelligence, construct a virtual simulation of Two. It can dream.

So that's what we have; awareness and appearance. There is no other element, and even appearance doesn't really exist, so for any question starting in *why*—Why is the sky blue? Why is there evil? Why doesn't mommy love me? Why am I strangling this parakeet?—the answer must be, *for the amusement of Brahman.*

It's the only possible answer.

✧

In the simplest sense, sense is the problem and nonsense is the solution. Nonsense, however, cannot be generated within a strictly logical system. There is no possibility of random chance, disorder, spontaneity, or chaos. Brahman does not play dice with Maya.

So, that's the setup. Maya, despite not existing, must perform the vital but impossible function of amusing Brahman. This is impossible because infinite consciousness is not capable of being finite, and perfect intelligence is not capable of being imperfect. Chaos is not possible, flaws and errors are not possible, irrationality and inaccuracy are not possible. Nonsense is not possible. The whole thing is perfect and cannot be rendered imperfect. The problem can't be fixed because there is no problem.

And that's the problem.

One Small Step

The fact that an opinion has been widely held is
no evidence whatever that it is not utterly absurd;
indeed in view of the silliness of the majority of
mankind, a widespread belief is more likely to be
foolish than sensible.

Bertrand Russell

N OW I WILL TELL YOU the secret of the Apollo moon
landings which is, there were none. No one has ever
gone to the moon. Based on what evidence do I reach this
conclusion: Waving flags? Misaligned shadows? *The Shining*?
Radiation? Any of the countless other telltales and giveaways
the moon-hoax community likes to point to? Happily, no,
we don't have to slog through the evidence, we can just look
with clear eyes and see that the real triumph of the Apollo
missions was quite different than the triumph proclaimed,
and of much greater interest to us here.

I don't know what's commonly believed about the moon landings when you're reading this, but when I'm writing it, most people still believe the narrative. Not that most people have revisited the issue and reweighed the evidence and made an informed decision on the subject, just that you have to be a crackpot to think we didn't really go to the moon, and most people don't like to be thought of as crackpots. I myself don't happen to mind.

The reason for looking at big goofy conspiracies in a book called *Dreamstate* may not be obvious at first, but what is the dreamstate except a big goofy conspiracy? We like to think of ourselves as discriminating, but that little vanity bubble is easily popped. Being able to think and actually thinking are two very different things. That we *can* think doesn't mean we *do*. Not only are we *not* the cool, level-headed thinkers we like to believe we are, we are completely off the other end of the chart, and not just the dumbest or most emotional of us; *all* of us. The real teaching of the great religions is that we will believe any crazy shit as long as others believe it too, and we're all just as desperate to believe as the most brainwashed member of the most bizarro cult. This insane gullibility doesn't just apply to one or two areas of life, it's the very fabric of our existence. It's there to be seen wherever we look, so the power of delusion depends on us not looking.

So let's look.

✿

My reason for thinking the moon missions were faked is that the chances of success would have been unacceptably low and the price of failure outrageously high. That's it. The evidence of a hoax is both mountainous and amusing, but the odds against success and the price of failure are all you have to look at.

Consider just some of what would be required for a successful mission; launch, a quarter million mile trip each way including two unshielded trips through the Van Allen Belts, lunar landing, surviving temperature extremes and radiation, relaunch, recoupling, return trip, reentry, splashdown and recovery, all in the 1960s, all slapped together in frantic haste, and all with very little practical experience or history of success in even the simplest parts. Consider what all this really entails and you will have no problem seeing that when all the smart people with their pocket protectors and slide rules sat around a table and tried to calculate the odds, they had to agree that the probability of success came out microscopically close to zero.

Now recall that the entire purpose of the entire production was not scientific discovery or a valiant, last-ditch effort to save the Earth from a planet killing asteroid; it was just a massive war-like spending program disguised as a PR stunt. Kennedy promised it, big-money forces lobbied for it, the superiority of ideologies was at stake. Vastly more important than *actual* success, therefore, was the *appearance* of success, and the appearance was infinitely easier to accomplish than the actual.

❁

Let's take a minute to contemplate what failure would look like. It might look like American exceptionalism had turned the moon from mankind's romantic jewel of the evening sky into an orbiting graveyard and monument to human folly, basically ruining it for everyone forever. Or, it might look like the corpses of American heroes doing laps around the Earth until they burned up on reentry, or a shiny coffin sailing out into the cosmos like a grisly interstellar greeting card, or our heroic boys coming home to parades and glory only to die horribly within a few months from radiation poisoning, a young Barbara Walters striking ratings gold with her bedside interviews.

In short, one absolutely hideous outcome after another, all the extreme antithesis of the vainglorious objectives of the program in the first place, and one of them almost certain to occur. Failure was not only an option, it was inevitable, and instead of proving the superiority of democracy over communism, as it was supposedly meant to do, the Apollo program would make America look criminally and comically inept until the end of time.

✿

It's not really the moon landings we're talking about, by the way, they're completely irrelevant. There is no such thing as non-fiction to me, so analyzing the Apollo program is the same as analyzing a movie or a dream. Apollo is worth looking at here because it's all about perception and emotion and reason and all sorts of fun stuff that aligns perfectly with our larger theme of how easily you can fool all of the people all of the time.

When you weigh the likelihood of a hoax against the claim of six successful landings and one spectacularly successful failure, the conclusion you arrive at really depends on you.

You might waver back and forth several times a day, or you might lock onto one side or the other and stay there. Reason plays a distant second to emotion in this, as in everything. When I was looking into this stuff a few years ago based on evidence and common sense, I went back and forth depending on what I was looking at. That's what made it fun, both sides are very compelling.

But when you step back from the evidence and see the whole thing with even a small amount of detachment, then a different way of weighing likelihoods emerges and a pretty firm conclusion can be arrived at. This doesn't require an uncommon spiritual perspective, just a bit of objectivity. As with other transparent conspiracies, you don't have to look with the eyes of an expert, you just have to look. It's hard to achieve a balanced viewpoint from *within* the debate, but step back, *one small step,* and the whole thing unfolds for you. No, the moon landings are not of any interest to us here, but stepping back from egoic distortion to see with clear eyes is.

✿

So now, put yourself in the executive-level meetings, the highest ones where final go/no-go decisions are made. Put the President in the room, that's the level of meeting we're talking about. In fact, *you're* the President, how's that? And keep in mind that this isn't just another space mission, this is the *big* one; the one it's all been about, the one the whole world will be watching, the one for all mankind. The stakes couldn't be higher. The cost of failure would vastly outweigh any benefit of success.

So, you're the president, you have to decide. You ask the

top experts at the table to bottom-line it for you. "What," you ask, "are the odds?"

You're the one who has to give the thumbs up, so think about it; what odds would you accept? What level of assurance would these homicidal bumblers need to provide before you'd greenlight a project in which failure would shame your nation and legacy forever? Would you say yes to a sixty percent chance of success? When is this meeting being held? If it's in 1967, then, as President, keep in mind that three astronauts, including a program whistleblower, were just burned to death during a launch rehearsal that was not considered dangerous.

What if they tell you seventy percent? Meaning only a thirty percent chance that the whole deal doesn't end in lasting national shame and an effortless victory for the Soviet Union. How about eighty percent? Meaning only a one-in-five chance that whenever anyone looks at the moon, all they'll think of is those clean-cut boys America sacrificed to national vanity. What if they tell you there's a ninety percent chance of success? Being not a total idiot yourself, you take anything these agenda-driven experts tell you with enough grains of salt to stop your heart. A ninety percent chance of success, you figure, might be more like point zero nine.

So what odds would you accept?

Try to take into account the ethos of the time, the realistic chances of success, how much you trust your so-called experts, and the horrific consequences of failure. When you weigh all the factors, there's really no choice. So now you, the President of the United States of America, respond the only way you possibly can.

"Hell no," you say, "screw Kennedy's legacy. Thumbs down, scrub it. I don't know if you NASA boys are stupid or crazy, but if you think I'm gonna let you go ahead with this cocka-mamie scheme and make this country the laughing stock of the world for countless generations, then I reckon you're about as dumb as a box of moon rocks. There's no way in hell this thing could ever work and if it backfires it'll represent a grotesque act of national hubris from which this country will never recover. And frankly, I don't believe you people know what the hell you're doing anyway. I wouldn't trust you eggheads to wind my watch. You just barbecued three of our boys in one of your little tin cans. If I need some blooper reels I'll call you. Now get the hell out of my office!"

✿

But they don't get out of your office, do they?

No. In fact, the head guy sitting across from you doesn't even seem surprised by your decision.

"Yes sir," he says, "but did I mention Plan B?"

Now you, as President, finally get it. These guys never thought you'd go for Plan A. They know just as well as you do that the whole idea is just pie-in-the-sky nonsense. It's called a door-in-the-face technique; they make you one offer knowing you're going to slam the door on them, and then they make another offer, the *real* offer, which by contrast looks pretty good. You see that this whole pitch has just been a setup for the real plan they came to sell.

"What's Plan B?" you ask.

"Well, sir," he replies, "Plan B is we just fake the whole thing. Hire some movie people and shoot it on a soundstage.

Only a handful of people would ever know the truth."

"Are you completely out of your goddamn mind?" you scream in a reasonable tone.

"Uh, strangely enough, no sir," he says, "I don't think so. Plan B would have about a hundred percent chance of success and a zero percent chance of littering the night sky with dead Americans. Plan B has many precedents for success and no failures, and of course, we have Hollywood. Plan B offers all of the benefits and none of the risk. You're absolutely correct that an *actual* moon mission would be astronomically likely blow up in our faces, but bullshitting is right in our wheelhouse, sir. After all, Mr. President, we are the government, it's what we do."

And maybe bullshit makes sense to you. Maybe the whole reason you're the one making this decision in the first place is because you were put in office by a *coup d'etat* that got completely bullshitted over. Maybe you launched a war in response to a false flag incident that you knew was total bullshit. So now you, as President, are not being asked to approve a loony-tunes moon mission, but some good old American bullshit with the promise of an ideological and space-race triumph. So now it's a no-brainer. You give the thumbs up, and they agree to name a space center after you.

✿

So that's my little theory and some of how I got there. (You should see my list, *Thirty-Three Reasonably Reasonable Reasons to Question the Moon Landings*, which I decided not to include in the back of this book because, seriously, who cares?) Maybe they faked it so successfully the first time that they went ahead and faked a second one, but no one was interested anymore and funding was drying up, so they faked a very dramatic, tightly scripted space emergency that had everyone back on the edge of their seats, complete with a miraculous Hollywood ending.

And then there were four more moon landings, six total, producing thousands of wonderful photographs of the lunar surface which could all be faked, but none of the stars, which couldn't. Why not adjust the exposure settings, stand in the shade, and aim the camera up? *Bam!* Proof you were there. And what better use of the moon than as a celestial observatory? If you can get dune buggies up there, you can probably manage a photographic telescope, and then have something other than rocks to show for all that work. I'm no expert, of course, but I'd think that if you claim to have gone to the moon six times you should be able to prove it, especially since it would be as simple as taking a few pictures of the stars.

✷

I prefer my theory of the moon landings over the accepted narrative even though, as a kid in the sixties, I was very swept up in the whole thing. I had the astronauts' pictures on my walls, I had a small library about NASA and the Apollo missions, I followed all this stuff closely. In 1969 I was almost as into Apollo as I was the Mets, which was a lot.

My interest in Apollo now is for entertainment purposes only. Am I sure there were no moon landings? It's the dream-state, you can't be sure of anything, but it's fun to peek behind the curtain and, who knows, maybe get a book chapter out of it. The fun is in the unraveling, in the seeing with fresh eyes; it's not pleasant to look upon the emperor in all his inglorious nudity, but it's instructive.

Little conspiracies like Apollo and 9/11 and Kennedy—like the bigger conspiracies of science, propaganda, religion, advertising, politics and other forms of mass indoctrination and delusion—have a lot to teach us about ourselves, if we care to look. That's the real takeaway here. We can step back, disengage our emotional attachments, and try to see how things appear on their own merit. It's not easy to peer through the fog. We have to want to look, know where to look, and be able to look, and even then we're rewarded not with a clear view of the object of our attention, but the realization that the only thing behind the swirling fog is more fog.

What's for Dinner

Granted, granted I'm a babbler, a harmless, irksome
babbler, as we all are. But what's to be done if the sole
and express purpose of every intelligent man is babble
— that is, a deliberate pouring from empty into void.

Fyodor Dostoyevsky, Notes from Underground

WHAT WAS I THINKING? Oh yeah, dinner. What would
be good? Fondue? Fondue. Fondue? We could do
fondue. Do people still do fondue? We did fondue, when?
Seventies? The seventies, Jesus. Carter, power, turn off the
lights. Ford, gas, Nixon. Disco. Geez. Cheese? Cheese
fondue? Yuck. Meat fondue? Yuck. Chocolate fondue? I don't
think we did chocolate. With what, marshmallows? That
sounds disgusting. Did we really eat that? I didn't.

"Oh shit, did I forget my keys?"

No, idiot, they're right there, hanging out of the thing. We
had that red enameled fondue thing with those long sharp
pointy things. It worked on canned fuel like bums drink.

Really? That doesn't sound right. Never make eye contact
with the bums in the train station, son, you'll never shake
'em off. Bums were different back then.

Need new wipers. Hot oil and pointy sticks, Jesus, fondue is really dangerous. You can't let kids near something like that. Not these days. I wonder where it is. Probably in the basement, on the shelves, in a box marked something. We used it that night mom wore the green dress. Meat. Yuck. Another dress was green too, or blue, maybe gray. In the basement, in a box marked something. That's gone now. Gone where? New home. Junk store. Landfill. Does it still exist? Crushed. Rusted. Maybe it no longer exists. Just gone. Like it never was. *Gone* gone. It wasn't, then was, now it's not. Just a memory, just a thought. Pretty deep thoughts. I can be deep. Is this guy ever gonna turn?

"C'mon buddy. First day? You can do it. Attaboy."

Maybe it's on a shelf somewhere, an antique. It should have a warning for kids. Don't spill burning oil in your lap. Lawsuit.

"Don't wait for them, just go. Oops, sorry. My bad."

The stuff from my life is now antiques, that's weird. Probably something. Seventies kitsch. Kitchen kitsch. Something something. Got hauled off. Goodwill something. Hunting. Who hauled it? Whose job is that? Hauling off people's crap like that? Seven already? All the stuff from a life and then one day it has to go and they have people for that. Pull up in a truck. Carry stuff out. Junk store. Fifty cents. Maybe it's in another basement now. If it still exists. Still red. Museum. Junk museum. Shelf. If what still exists? Fondue? Not safe. We're not doing fondue for dinner. You spill that thing and everyone's on fire. Everyone applying burn cream forever because of jackass fondue. Now think for real. Think. What? Oh, ribs. Ribs? Ribs. Ribs? Ribs. Okay, ribs. Call it in, pick them up. Get all greasy. Happy dogs. Happy everyone. Make a mess.

"What are you looking at buddy? Try looking at yourself. Who let you out?"

Ribs? Are ribs healthy? Is anything? Who knows? What can you do? You can try eating right but you never know. Butter eggs good. Butter eggs bad. Can't keep track. Why try? Coffee, red wine, chocolate, shut up. They say they know but they don't. No one knows anything.

"C'mon lady. Am I the only one who knows how to drive? Let's make an effort people."

I should probably drink raw milk but that's a nuisance. Cow or goat? Human? Yuck. Why does human sound gross? Cow or goat should sound gross. Human should sound normal. Sounds gross, though. Don't want to picture the dairy. What time is it? Shit, did I miss my turn? Maybe it would help to vocalize.

"Shit."

Where's my head? Eating right, nuisance. Every single thing can't be a nuisance. Oh, there, ribs on the sign. That's auspicious. That's a sign. The universe is telling me to get ribs. Why do they keep bringing the McRib back? Those things suck. Look at that picture. The meat's disgusting, the bread's disgusting, the sauce is disgusting. What does that leave? The pickle. Children probably died to bring us that pickle. Little kids picking pickles. Poor little pickle pickers. Jesus, am I getting bitter? I should turn on the radio so I don't have to listen to my stupid thoughts all the time. You can't find good bread anymore. People don't even know what bread is anymore. Edible sponge. That's an interesting thought. I'm an interesting guy. I like ribs. Ribs are good. Not a nuisance. Probably full of bad pharma corporate greed Monsanto estrogen glycosyl growth stuff so fish have brains on the outside, but not a nuisance. Okay, ribs. That's pretty good thinking. I'm a pretty good thinker. I have a problem, I think about it, I find a solution. What's for dinner? Ribs. *Bam!* Good work. Just get in there and figure it out. Why junk everything up with a million stupid thoughts?

"No right on red? Seriously?"

Jesus, what's that? Oh, hunger. Ribs. So, okay, ribs then. That's how you make a decision. How many meals in life? Fifty thousand? Okay, this one is ribs. Settle down. Lighten up. No store. No cart. No people. No line. No paper or plastic. Jesus, don't talk to me. All this talking is completely unnecessary. Nice in the car, quiet, no one yapping all the time. I do my best thinking in the car. Ribs good, good thought. We'll have alfalfa tomorrow night. What's alfalfa? Is that food? The kid with the hair thing. Spanky? No, Alfalfa. Duh. What was the black kid? There were a few. Buckwheat? Eddie Murphy. Is that racist? Was Buckwheat racist? Maybe it wasn't Buckwheat. Buckwheat pancakes and alfalfa salad. Spanky, Darla, little Baretta, Froggy, that other kid. Am I a racist? I can't tell what's racist. Maybe everything is racist. If everything is racist then nothing is racist and everyone can relax. Problem solved. What's wrong with the world? Is it me? Are ribs racist? Jesus, I didn't think of that. Noodles? Are noodles racist? Depends what kind, maybe. Fifty thousand meals, right? What, they're all supposed to be perfect? Gimme a break. Okay, this one's a little racist, maybe. Or maybe *thinking* it's racist is racist, or maybe not knowing.

What race am I? Is white a race or the absence of race? I should know this one.

"That's not a parking space, Chumley. Let's move along. There's a good fella."

Probably a race. Caucasoid? Okay, too much. You can't go through all this for every stupid meal. Fifty thousand. That's a lot. You can't think this much about every single one. Try thinking about something useful. Is the rib place even open on Mondays? It's not Monday. You have to cut out all the extra thinking and just make a decision. That's what everybody should do and then everything would make more sense. You wouldn't have all the craziness. That whole Middle East thing, that's pretty crazy. Also the news. And what about sports? Gosh.

"Ow. Ow. Ow."

Shit, did I bite my tongue? When did that happen? I hope I'm not getting a thing. Uh oh, there's a cop, be cool. Act normal. Cool? Cool. Is he looking at me? Don't look. Okay, he's gone. Do people still say cool? What a drag. What a drag? Sixties, what a trip, missed it all. Where was I? Oh yeah, the news and all the news stuff and all the stuff in the news. Geez, I don't like thinking about the news, all the news stuff. There was that one thing on the news, that guy did that thing, that was okay, but I'm gonna sneeze. Here it comes. Where'd it go? Russia? Russia in the news, Greece, Nepal. Nepal? Where's that? What else is over there? Bangladesh? Bhutan? That's it, Bhutan. Bunai? Is that a place? Brunei? Is that a country? Bhopal. That's a city. That's where they had that thing, the corporate evil poison gas thing.

"C'mon folks, let's pick it up a little. You, lady on the phone,

I think you can do better."

What's the fine for hitting a pedestrian? I could afford a few. Jesus, good thing no one can hear what I'm thinking. They'd think I was a dick. Oh man, a racist dick. Oh man? Oh man. Amen. Amen? Omen. Oman. Oman? Is that a country? It's always in the crossword puzzle. Oman? Omar? Imam? Emir? Something like that. Emu? Flightless bird. Jesus, there's like seven of them. Swimless fish? Walkless dog? Crossword puzzle words. You never need them anywhere else. Hebrew months. What? I'm supposed to memorize them? One stupid blank square left because I don't know Esau's wife's mother's donkey's middle name? Shut up. I get penalized for not knowing that? How good do I want to be at puzzles anyway? Like what, the best? What for? Then I have to go around and be the best at crossword puzzles all the time? What a drag. Good enough is good enough. That's a good motto. Not a great motto, but good enough.

"Good enough is good enough."

Sounds good, sounds wise. Geez, you got so much stuff to think about, you can't go around being the super master of everything all the time. Maybe one or two things, but not everything. Good enough is good enough.

"Jesus, what's that smell? Is that me?"

Oh, no, it's that truck, thank God. Good enough. Good enough is good enough. That's a good motto. Super motto, super duper. Get it on a t-shirt. Tattoo. Where? Someplace it won't look dumb when I'm old and fat. Get laughed at during my autopsy. Shoulder. No, that should be mom or a flag or some cool Chinese symbol, something deep, don't tell. Aborigines. I bet they have some cool symbols. Are aborigines negroid? Australian ones. They look negroid. Is negroid racist? No, it's the name of the race, isn't it? Negroid, caucasoid, rhomboid, thyroid, deltoid. What are Eskimos? Mongoloid? Jesus, that's *gotta* be racist. Am I an Eskimo racist? Mike Tyson's face. Shit, there's another black people thing. Oh man, do I have a black people thing? Oh man? Oman? Omar? Omar and Chalky are the same guy. Tattoos don't look good on black people. White people either. They look like birth marks. Burns. Fondue burns. What would mom look like on a tattoo? Or a tattoo on mom? Or a mom tattoo on mom? Why don't women get mom tattoos? Why do I drink so much coffee? Do I even like it? I don't know what I like.

"Wrong lane, maestro."

I like young Elliot Gould but I don't *like* him like him, I just like him. That's not weird. Marlowe, Hawkeye, that other thing. Coffee is good for me. Maybe good. Probably bad. Oh, there she is, that picture. Green dress? Black and white. Where was that? Club? Maybe. Did I dream it? Where is it now? Boxes. Box marked something. Pictures maybe. Basement, shelves, fondue pot, hauled off. Weird. Itch? Itch. Itch? Why do my ribs itch? Oh yeah, ribs. Universe reminding me. Smart universe. Next left. Make the call. Yeah, okay. Ribs. Ribs? Loofa. Loofa? How do you know when to replace a loofa? Jesus, I bet those things get gross. You never want to look at anything too close. Can you clean them? Maybe boil them? Boiled loofa. Looks like noodles. I'm hungry. What was I thinking? Oh yeah, dinner. What would be good? Fondue. Fondue? Fondue. No, wait. . . .

Alice in the Machine

Most people believe the mind to be a mirror, more
or less accurately reflecting the world outside of them,
not realizing on the contrary that the mind is itself the
principal element of creation.

Rabindranath Tagore

"I IMAGINE THAT RIGHT NOW, you must be feeling a bit like Alice, tumbling down the rabbit hole."

"Yes," replied Alice demurely, "you might say that."

"It's like a splinter in your mind," said the hairless black giant with looking-glass eyes sitting in the shabby leather chair opposite her. Alice looked down and saw to her dismay that her blue puffed-sleeve dress and white pinafore and ankle-strap shoes were now made entirely of shiny black leather.

"*What's* like a splinter in my mind?" she asked. "And *who*, might I ask, are *you?* And *where*, might I also ask, am *I?* And *how*, might I lastly ask, did I *get* here?"

"My name is Morpheus," said the enormous leather-clad creature. "And *this*," he said with dramatic flair, "is the Matrix."

"And *what*," said Alice with equal flair, "is the Matrix?"

"*That*," said the hairless giant, "is the question."

"I *know* it's the question," said a somewhat exasperated Alice, "I just *asked* it. How did I get here?"

"You have never been anywhere else."

Alice craned her head around to survey the room and found it not so very familiar.

"Not the room," said the latest addition to the ever-expanding stable of Alice's imaginarium, "the world, reality, you know, *everything.*"

Alice harrumphed and crossed her little arms and settled more deeply into her chair.

"You have the look of a little girl who accepts what she sees because she's expecting to wake up. Ironically, this is not far from the truth."

Alice, like any well-read girl of her age, knew exactly what the word ironically meant, and the fact that she could not summon that knowledge at the moment only added to her growing vexation.

"Let me tell you why you're here," said Morpheus, a name which, if Alice recalled correctly, meant either God of Dreams or Death by Boredom.

"Kindly do," said Alice tersely, feeling that the conversation could be zipping along at a much zippier clip.

"You're here because you know something."

"Yes indeedle-doodle," said Alice, trying to make the conversation funner since she couldn't make it faster. "Yes, indeedle-doodle, I do!"

Alice liked the sound of that so much she made it a song:

> I know that fish fly in the water,
> And birds swim in the air.
> I know that cats can smile,
> And have eight lives to spare.
> I know you cannot tame a shrew,
> I know it through and through.
> Yes, I know a thing or two,
> Indeedle-doodle, I do!
>
> I know that turtles fly around,
> And pigs will often leave the ground.
> I know that curious creatures abound,
> And disappear when I make a sound.
> I know that me and you make two,
> And the world is just a great big zoo.
> Yes, I know a thing or two,
> Indeedle-doodle, I do!
>
> But what I do *not* seem to know,
> And what I hope to be *shown*,
> Is if you *can't* get to the point,
> Or if you simply *won't*.
> That's a thing I do *not* know,
> Indeedle-doodle, I *don't*!

"Yes, well, what you know, you can't explain," Morpheus continued when Alice had finished her song. "You are a slave. You were born into bondage, a prison that you cannot smell, taste, or touch. A prison for your mind."

"I thought the Hatter was mad," thought Alice, squirming

in her seat, "but this creature takes the tea cake!"

"But you feel it," continued Morpheus, in response to her rolling hand gesture, "you felt it your entire…"

"Look, sorry, but if I might be so unforgivably rude as to interrupt you," said Alice, unable to muster another ounce of patience. "I can see you have a lovely speech prepared, but I was wondering, if it wouldn't be *too* excruciating for you, if we might not just skip down to the meaty bits."

Alice watched, head atilt, as the dusky giant began verbally scrolling down through his mental document. "…uh, yeah, sure, let's see, uh, something wrong with the world… you don't know what it is… like a splinter in your mind…"

"Yes!" cried Alice with a merry clap of her hands. "I think that's where I came in. And why specifically do I have this rather disagreeable splinter?"

"…driving you mad," the curious creature completed his recitation.

"The splinter still?" said Alice. "Yes, driving me a bit mad. So, if we might press on?"

"Do you know what I'm talking about?"

"Oh dear me!" cried Alice inwardly, "this creature is worse than the Caterpillar for getting to the point!"

"Well," said Alice in her most politest little voice, "could it be that Matrix thing you mentioned such a long time ago?"

"Do you want to know what it is?"

Alice maintained an outer calm while holding back a rising wave of pique. She allowed herself a few stiff eye-blinks before replying.

"Yes, Mr. Morpheus, if it's not too much bother."

"The Matrix is everywhere, it's all around us, even in this

room. It is the world that has been pulled over your eyes to blind you from the truth."

"Yes, okay, fine, yes?"

"Unfortunately," said Morpheus, "no one can be told what the Matrix is."

Alice took the opportunity afforded by Morpheus' dramatic pause to draw a deep breath and count slowly down from ten.

"Well, we might have started there, mightn't we?" said Alice, unsure whether, in her present state of miff, she mightn't be using the word *mightn't* other than correctly.

"You have to see it for yourself."

"Longest are the roads that lead to beginnings," thought Alice, and reminded herself to write that down later in case it was wise.

Morpheus held out a red pill in one hand and a blue pill in the other.

"Let me guess," said Alice drily, "one pill makes me larger and one pill makes me small?"

"This is your last chance," said Morpheus. "After this, there is no going back."

"Let's move this along, shan't we?" She was pretty sure she was using the word *shan't* all wrong, but she shan't cared.

"You take the blue pill and the story ends. You wake in your bed and believe whatever you want to believe."

Alice wiggled her tiny feet impatiently.

"You take the red pill and you stay in Wonderland and I show you how deep the rabbit-hole goes."

Alice was somewhat chagrined to find her own adventures once more the stuff of milquetoast metaphor.

"Remember," said Morpheus solemnly, "all I am offering is the truth. Nothing more."

That was all poor Alice could endure. She could contain herself no longer.

"My dear Mr. Morpheus," she said, "between the two of us, I'm afraid it is *you*, sir, who has no idea how deep the rabbit-hole goes. You are like the man who has traveled one town over and thinks he has reached the end of the world, whereas I have traveled entire worlds and think I have yet to leave home. It is *you*, Mr. Morpheus, that should be swallowing your red pill, and another after that, and another and another. A journey of a thousand miles may *begin* with a single step, but does not *end* with it. You dangle from but a shallow root, my long-winded friend, and I suggest you release it and see for *yourself* how deep the rabbit hole goes."

Now, for the first time, Alice noticed a looking glass next to her chair. She reached out to touch it and watched her fingers disappear beneath the rippling surface.

"Oh, thank God!" she squealed, and oozed herself through the mirror to resume her adventure.

Battlefield Promotion

Perhaps all the dragons of our lives are
princesses who are only waiting to see
us once beautiful and brave.

Rainer Maria Rilke

W<small>E'RE EXPECTING A STORM</small> to come in from the south-west, so we angle our lounges that way and get comfortable. The last time we were together, we'd been remembering her father, so we just picked back up from there as if there hadn't been a two week interval.

"My father was worried that he didn't understand you," says Lisa once we're settled and speaking of our past. "I think he thought you might be a dangerous influence on me and Maggie. He was a little adrift after my mother passed. He was always a bit loosely wrapped, especially compared to her, but I remember that he seemed worried about getting involved with you, getting his family involved with you, like he might have summoned something that was too much for him, like the Sorcerer's Apprentice. I wondered if he regretted it."

"He didn't," I say.

"He didn't what," she asks. "Regret it?"

"He didn't get me involved with your family."

"Well, I mean, through your books or whatever. When he was working on the sequel to *Cosmic Consciousness* and he came across your books."

I pause like someone who hears a click and wonders if he just stepped on a mine.

"That's not what happened, or it didn't happen until a few years later." I take a moment to consider the situation. "I thought you knew all this. It was your mother who first got in touch with me. Your father got to me from her."

"My *mother?* Oh, I don't think so. You never even met my mother. My mother? No way."

I wait.

"What, you're not kidding? My mother? You knew my mother?"

"Not in person. We had a brief correspondence, which actually included *her* father, technically."

"Shut up," she advises.

I do, but it's her mouth that's hanging open.

"No way," she shakes her head. "No, I doubt that very much."

She stares at me for a long moment, then stands up and starts pacing in fits and starts. Beyond her, the dark clouds are making a promise they're slow to deliver.

"Jesus, Jed, what the hell are you talking about? You have a secret history with my family?"

"I thought you knew."

"Knew *what?*" she asks in kind of a pushy, lawyer way.

"After the first book came out, your mother got in touch with me regarding some questions she had about her father."

She stares at me in that way of staring she has.

"Are you messing with me? Her father died in the war, the Spanish Civil War. My mother was like the most tightly wound person I've ever known and you're like… I don't even *know* what you are. I can't even picture you and my mother in the same… *anything.*"

"We never met. Your mother contacted me, by mail. She had questions and thought I might have the answers."

"She thought you might have answers? And did you?"

"Yes."

"To what questions?"

"She had a stack of letters from her father, from the war. Do you know about them?"

"No."

"They were letters her father had written to her while he was away at war. They had obviously been very important to her, but she never really understood them. Somehow, she came across *Damnedest* and thought I might be able to help."

"And you helped her?"

"Yes."

"Jesus, I never knew about any of this. I always thought it was my father who reached out to you with all those emails about philosophy and creating a course based on your book and free and easy access and all that."

"No, it was your mother, a few years earlier. Then your father started emailing me, then your mother died but I never heard about that. This is all like fifteen years ago. I think that's how it happened."

"Jesus, I can't process this. You know, my mother's family was like Spanish nobility."

"Uh, yeah, I got that."

Maya jumps up on the chaise and nestles in between my legs. I play with her ears and watch Lisa trying to make sense of this new chapter in her history.

"Her father," she says, "I never met him, obviously, but he was like a member of the gentry or something, a landowner. She never really talked about him. She was like two or three years old when he died, so you're saying he was writing letters to a toddler?"

"I guess."

She's pacing, thinking, processing, cross-examining me. It's kind of fun to watch.

"Her family came to America after he died. They had to get away from Franco. They lost everything. Do you know all this?"

"I don't recall."

"Really? I thought you had that weird memory, all the poetry. What about the letters? Do you recall them?"

"She sent them to me. They were in Castilian, of course, and they were in very bad physical shape, as you might imagine. I had someone read them to me, enough to understand what I was hearing and to answer your mother's questions. It didn't take long. I wrote her a letter, she sent me a thank you note, and that was it. A few years later I started getting emails from your father who, I assume, heard about me from her."

"Do you still have her letters?"

"No."

"You didn't keep them?"

"I don't keep anything," I say. "Well," I amend, rubbing Maya's nose, "her."

"How would my mother have found your book?"

"No idea. She asked, the universe answered."

"And you sent her father's letters back to her?"

"Yes."

"I've been through all her stuff, I never saw them."

"Maybe she built a nice fire and threw them in."

"Why would she do that?"

"I might have suggested it, but I don't know if that's what she did."

"Why would you have suggested it?"

"Fire good."

"Wow. And she was satisfied with your explanation about her father's letters?"

"Of course."

"Of *course?*"

"Well, my explanation was obviously correct. She might have suspected as much when she got in touch with me, but she wanted to confirm it. It was pretty obvious."

"What was obvious? That her father didn't like war? That he missed his baby daughter?"

Lightning is visible in the distance. Thunder can be more felt than heard.

"The letters were your grandfather's process of spiritual autolysis. They weren't just the record of his transition, but the actual vehicle of it. Somehow your mother heard about spiritual autolysis—she used the term in her original letter—and tracked me down and asked me and I told her, yes, this was your father's process of awakening as described in *Damnedest.*

It took the form of letters to a baby daughter, but it was really how he was undergoing his own egoic dissolution."

She displays the thousand-mile stare I remember from years earlier. I wait.

"You mean, my grandfather was, what, enlightened? He was like you?"

"It depends on how long he lived after the last letter I saw, but I would say yes, that he probably completed the initial process. A battlefield promotion, of sorts."

"I mean, *enlightened* enlightened? Like *you* mean it? Like, awake from the dreamstate? Truth-realized and all that?"

"Well, keeping in mind that it's not really a spiritual thing. It's a natural life process, and once it starts it doesn't stop."

"But why? Because of the war?"

"That was certainly a factor. Extreme duress is very conducive to the awakening process. War would be a kind of highly compressed reality, much more intense than, you know, sitting around an ashram or whatever."

"What other factors were there?"

"No idea."

"Oh my God, this is too much."

She drinks her wine and sets it down. She sits down and stands back up. She stands with hands on hips like she's about to scold me, then starts pacing again. Behind her, our storm is lurking just out of sight.

"Most of the letters were very powerful and distinctly inappropriate for a child," I continue, "and they weren't really letters to a daughter anyway. It's more like they were his response to a series of increasingly powerful epiphanies that were coming at him too fast to handle, so by necessity, he discovered the value of writing. He may have used the writing not just to think, but to process volcanic emotions. He was probably bursting to express what he was going through but couldn't share it with his fellow soldiers, so he wrote these very powerful outpourings that were only thinly disguised as letters to a baby daughter."

"But why? Why disguise them at all? Why not just write a diary?"

"The process of spiritual autolysis, of using writing to focus and magnify our powers of reason and to process overwhelmingly powerful and complex emotions, is naturally enhanced when done for an intended recipient or audience, but not necessarily someone who would ever read or reply. In fact, preferably not. I did it like a book for an imagined audience. I wrote more than a dozen drafts and burned them all. Melville did it as a book in one big, messy draft. Some people have used me as the recipient. A child real or imagined, an unseen friend, an idealized teacher, someone from your past; it helps to feel that you're actually teaching or sharing, then the process works much better than if you were just doing it for yourself. When you're in it, it feels like it has to be that way."

"And his experience, my grandfather's, was more like you? Not what I went through?"

"Yes, your grandfather's experience was greatly intensified by circumstances. He probably experienced a violent awakening before setting pen to paper. The writing was his attempt to make sense of the process as it unfolded."

"You make it sound like he was a victim of it."

"That's always how it is."

Her pacing is at odds with the calm evening and the fire and the wine. It's supposed to be raining but stubbornly isn't. If I could set the background, like on a computer screen, I'd call for some storm drama at this point, like a digital Prospero summoning the tempest.

"So it's just a coincidence that I went through my thing and you came along and now here's my grandfather who I never met but he's somehow... I mean, *really?* This is all like some big coincidence?"

"I'm not a coincidence guy like you mean it, like something irregular or unlikely. I'm more of a pattern guy."

"Meaning?"

"To me, from my perspective, everything coincides, everything flows together. There's harmony, energetic alignment, pattern."

"Okay, okay, is that everything? Christ, is there anything else?"

"Please sit down."

"What?"

"You might be more comfortable sitting," I say.

She goes into her hard stare mode again and doesn't sit. I continue anyway.

"Okay, I actually have a very weak memory," I say, "like a muscle I don't use anymore. My weird memory, as you call it, is something from when I was a kid, and it wasn't that weird. Poetry took on a music in my head and I retained it. Mainly when I was young, but also later, like with your grandfather's last letter which I probably remember because it was not part of his process, but a goodbye to someone who had become very important to him, I think, in his thoughts, in his most challenging times."

Now she sits.

"You memorized his last letter?"

"I made a copy. I carried it and read it once in awhile. It got stuck in my head."

"In Spanish or English?"

"Spanish. I don't even remember the exact meaning, but the general meaning is clear. I think he knew that he had arrived at the end of his process and basically knew that he was finished with this life. That was my sense of it."

"Okay. Jesus. Can you tell me?"

"It's possible that I've altered it over time, but I can try."

I run through it in my head to makes sure it's all there. I lean back and close my eyes and recite from my weird memory as she translates from her sketchy Spanish.

"Querida Izzie," I say

"My dearest little Isabel" she says.

"Me temo que esta debe ser la última carta que te escriba."

"I fear that this is the last letter I will write to you."

"Has sido para mí fuente de gran felicidad en vida y de gran tristeza ahora que tengo que dejarla."

"You have been my source of great happiness in life and of great sadness now that I have to leave."

"Te ruego no te entristezcas por mí, sino que atesores mi recuerdo y pienses en mí en los momentos tranquilos."

"I ask you not be sad for me, but cherish my memory and think of me in quiet moments."

"He cambiado y ahora soy distinto a la última vez que te besé las mejillas y la frente."

"I have changed and now I am different from the last time

I kissed your cheeks and forehead."

"Ojalá pudiera decir que he ganado algo de sabiduría para poder dejarte en herencia, pero soy menos sabio ahora de lo que lo he sido nunca."

"I wish I could say I've gained some wisdom to leave you as an inheritance, but am less wise now than I have ever been."

"Vive tu vida, ángel mío, sé valiente y feliz y recuerda reír y bailar y confiar siempre en tu corazón."

"Live your life, my angel, be brave and happy and remember to laugh and dance and always trust your heart."

"Algún día tendrás un bebé y entonces conocerás la alegría que trajiste a mi corazón."

"Someday you'll have a baby and you shall know the joy you have brought to my heart."

"Adiós, mi hija querida. Tu padre que te quiere."

"Goodbye, my dear child. Your father that loves you."

✿

Lisa sits quietly for a few moments before getting up and going inside. Now the storm arrives, having missed its cue by several minutes. I repeat the Spanish version to myself like a song.

The Parable of the Coyote

"How can the coyote reach outside except by thrusting
through the wall? To me, the roadrunner is that wall,
shoved near to me. Sometimes I think there's naught
beyond, but 'tis enough. She tasks me; she heaps me; I
see in her outrageous strength, with an inscrutable malice
sinewing it. That inscrutable thing is chiefly what I hate;
and be the roadrunner agent, or be the roadrunner
principal, I will wreak that hate upon her."

Wile E. Coyote, Genius

O NE DAY YOU'RE SITTING AROUND in the state we're
calling asleep-in-the-dream, sub-lucid, normal
waking consciousness. So what's wrong with that? Nothing
is wrong with that. How can anything be wrong when it's all
just appearance? There are no superior or inferior states, just
different states. There is no better place to be than where you
are. Until you think there is. Then there is.

And now, for some reason, you think there is.

Something changes. You discover that what you had always considered normal life is actually a bit strange and that nothing is quite what you thought. Until this minor awakening you were just living your normal everyday life, but now that normal life doesn't seem quite so normal, and neither do you. Now you have taken a step back from your life, one small step, and you are confused by what you see.

For one thing, you seem to spend an inordinate amount of time chasing a flightless bird. For another thing, you seem to dwell in an endless desert in which only you and the bird and a delivery truck and the occasional ill-timed locomotive seem to exist. Furthermore, as you examine your situation, you find it odd that you are a bipedal coyote and, odder still, that you are a cartoon. And now that you're taking a fresh look, you realize that your whole life is a cartoon, so that's pretty weird. How did you not see *that* before? In fact, now that you *do* see it, you can't believe you ever *didn't* see it, much less that you've gone your entire life without noticing you were a cartoon coyote in a cartoon desert chasing a cartoon bird, and aided in these efforts by a cartoon company that brings you whatever implements of bird murder your devious heart desires.

✿

All that most maddens and torments; all that stirs up the lees of things; all truth with malice in it; all that cracks the sinews and cakes the brain; all the subtle demonisms of life and thought; all evil, to crazy Coyote, were visibly personified, and made practically assailable in the roadrunner. He piled upon the bird's purple plumage the sum of

all the general rage and hate felt by his whole race;
and then, as if his chest had been a mortar, he
burst an Acme Birdshot Shell upon it.

✿

Which raises another issue: Why are you chasing the bird? Why does your entire existence revolve around such a ridiculous enterprise? You obviously aren't driven by hunger. If you can order rocket-powered roller skates, you can order a rotisserie chicken with slaw, some roasted potatoes, a chilled beverage and perhaps, if you're feeling naughty, a small parfait. What drives you in this mad compulsion? Is it hatred? Love? Lust? Ego? Why is there no *Mrs.* Coyote? And when exactly did you decide to make chasing a beepy-ass bird your entire life's purpose? You don't remember any actual decision, it's just what you do. There seem to be a lot of decisions being made around here, you notice, and you're not the one making them.

"If I didn't decide what I'm doing with my life," you sit on a rock in the thinker pose and ponder, "then whose life is it? I imagine that I possess free will, but who is this *I* to whom I refer? Is Coyote, Coyote? Is it I, God, or who, that lifts this paw?"

You lift your paw but receive no answer.

"And what," you continue in your newly awakened curiosity, "is all this cartoon shit anyway? This can't be right. Are there really only eight colors and two dimensions? Something's not kosher."

You may not see what's real, but you're starting to see what's not, and what's *not* real, you now see, is pretty much everything.

"In fact," you now realize, "I must have been drugged or disabled or otherwise hornswoggled to ever think this ridiculous cartoon universe was real."

Come to think of it, you always thought it was strange that the bird could run into a painted tunnel entrance while you just smashed into the rock wall, right before a train came barreling out and further smashed your already smashed ass. And what's with that gravity double-take thing every time you go off a cliff? And the ability to pull pre-made, situation-appropriate signs out of your butt? *Uh oh!* And what about all those traps that didn't work on the bird but worked perfectly on you? How many times have you been crushed or blown up or burnt to a crisp? It happens every time, and every time it happens, you pick yourself up, dust yourself off, start all over again.

"Bullshit!" you cry, at long last. "Bullshit!"

Bullshit is right. You may not know what *is* real yet, but now you know what's not, and this whole thing you always thought was your life is definitely not. All this time you thought you were the trickster, but you were always the tricked.

"There must be more to all this than meets the eye," you reason, for the first time using your brain for something outside your programming. "There must be something else," you continue, "a creator, a planner, a grand design, a superior intelligence… something beyond. There must be *more*."

✿

You don't know it yet, and it may take awhile to process,

but you have just destroyed the universe. Just like that, just that easily, you have taken one small step, and that's all it takes. You have peeled back the veil and looked behind the scenery and seen your world for the flat and unconvincing illusion it really is. The only thing that ever made it real was the emotional energy of your belief, but now that you've withdrawn your lifeforce, you see your reality for what it has been all along; a Looney Tunes production.

✿

Why, you wonder, are you so obsessed with catching a stupid bird? It's there, this desire, burning inside you like a torch, but who put it there? The only answer that matters, you realize, is that it wasn't you. You take a moment to reflect and discover that, burning desire aside, you have no particular feelings about the roadrunner at all. So what, you ask yourself, is the point of all this? *Cui bono?* Who benefits?

Good question.

And, you ask, is there really a bird at all? Is any of this real? Now that you've broken out of character, you're taking fresh stock of everything, and nothing is adding up like you thought it did.

So the next day you don't chase the bird, who, confused by this departure from the established patterns, approaches you. You ignore it. The Acme Corporation truck delivers the giant rubber band and the football helmet you ordered, but you take no notice.

"It's like I've been asleep my entire life," you muse as the bird pecks at your head. "I'm a smart guy, I can think, at least, I *think* I can think, so why didn't I figure this out before? It doesn't take a genius to see that none of this makes any sense. It's like I've been drunk or possessed or under a spell that made me chase the bird and never question anything, but as soon as I *do* question, even a little bit, the whole thing folds like a house of cards."

A lightbulb appears over your head.

"Jesus," you think, "I bet I'm not even a goddamn coyote!"

What then, you wonder, are you?

"Well, that's an interesting thought," you muse. "If I'm not what I think I am, then what am I? *Who* am I? What's behind the appearance? If my eyes tell one story and my mind another, which do I trust? If I continue to believe in appearances, then I must continue playing this ridiculous character in the absurd farce I call my life, but what if I allow my thoughts to override my senses? What if I think instead of feel? What if I follow the dictates of my mind instead of the urgings of my heart? What then?"

☼

So, congratulations are in order, or are they? You have achieved a major step toward liberation, or have you? Are you glad you did, or do you wish you didn't? Your old life didn't make much sense, but as long as you didn't know that, it didn't matter. But now you know, so now it does. Where are you going to live now that you've destroyed your cartoon world? Who will you be now that you've destroyed your cartoon character? What will you do now that you've seen the futility of action? This desert may be fake, but it's *where* you are. Your character may be a fiction, but it's *who* you are. Chasing the bird might be Sisyphean folly, but it gives your life a dramatic context, and your character is certainly designed to do it. So what are your options? You can go sit in the shade and refuse to play your part, or you can crawl back into character and chase the bird and get smashed and fried every day.

If those are the two horns of your dilemma, being bored in truth or engaged in a lie, then here's your *tertium quid*, the third option: Go. Escape the lie. Take all that emotional energy you were wasting on the bird and turn it to new purpose. Break out of character or die trying. Unzip your coyote costume and step out of it, peel back the corner of the frame and walk into whatever lies behind. Sometimes you think there's naught beyond, but even if there's not, at least you'll be out of this ridiculous desert and away from that shithead bird. If your life is a lie, you have nothing to lose.

But where can you go now? What can you do?

You can focus your attention on that one question you left unanswered: *Cui bono?* Who benefits? Somewhere out there is the animator who both defines and constrains you; that's your *real* roadrunner. That bastard needs some serious killing, and you're just the coyote for the job.

Or whatever the hell you are.

The Ballad of Ken & Barbie

No man ever believes that the Bible means
what it says: He is always convinced that it
says what he means.

George Bernard Shaw

I RETURN TO THE CABIN and find Maggie doing schoolwork
at the dining table. I go through my apres-walk routine
and get us both water before sitting on the hearth to remove
my shoes.

"What's up?" I ask.

"Homework," she grumbles. "Before I go back, I'm supposed to do a breakdown of the story of Adam and Eve. Do
you mind if I work here?"

"Of course not. What's a breakdown?"

"A report, I guess. Characters, plot, arc, all that."

"The *Bible* Adam and Eve?"

"Yeah, the creation myth, what else?"

"Maybe some movie or book or something. Why that?"

"I don't know, it was the most familiar one on the list I had to choose from. It sounded easy. I almost picked *Jekyll and Hyde* or the *Book of Job*."

"Is there anything interesting about Adam and Eve?"

"I was going to ask you that."

"I'm not a good go-to guy for Bible stuff."

"I thought there might be a Joseph Campbell or Carl Jung angle or something."

"I'm sure there is, but you'd have to ask them. Have you read it lately?"

"Yeah, a few versions, all pretty much the same. Adam, Eve, God, snake, apple, banished."

I flop onto the recliner, slam it into maximum comfort and close my eyes to enjoy the best part of a long walk. Maya settles in under the foot support where I'm afraid I'll some-day get up too fast and mechanically decapitate her. My body melts into the chair.

"I don't think I could contribute anything that would help you in your class," I mumble.

"I know," she says, "but it's such a boring project, I just wanted to try to make it interesting."

"That's what God said," I say drowsily.

"What?"

"Before you try to explain creation," I suggest, "you should try to prove it. You might save yourself a lot of trouble."

"Meaning what?"

"That if creation is a myth, then you don't need a creation myth."

"You're saying that creation doesn't exist?"

"Unless you know something I don't."

"Well then," she asks, "how do you explain all this?"

I can't see what she's referring to because my eyes are closed.

"Try to figure out what the essence of the story is," I say. "The characters and plot would be mostly irrelevant, just a vehicle for the core message."

"But what's the core message?"

"What?" I ask.

"What what?" she asks.

"Core message?"

"That was like an hour ago. You fell asleep."

"Oh, good."

"So what's the core message of Adam and Eve?" she asks.

"Oh yeah. I'd have to think about it, but I'd say it boils down to the transition they undergo."

"Like when they eat the apple?"

"What is the apple really called?"

"Specifically, it's the fruit of the tree of the knowledge of good and evil."

"Okay, so I guess the question is, what does good and evil mean? It sounds like generic naughty and nice, but that doesn't really fit."

"Yeah, I don't know. After they eat the apple they realize they're naked and feel shame, and they can suffer and get sick and die."

"Well, if that's the case then it's not a creation myth, more like an affliction myth, which wouldn't be very interesting."

"Nuts."

"I seem to remember that if you cite the parable of the light under the bushel as precedent, you could argue that good means awake and evil means asleep."

"You mean, awake and asleep like *you* mean?"

"Maybe. Look it up."

There's no internet in the cabin so she does it the old fashioned way. It takes a few minutes during which I think about how nice the universe was to give me this chair.

"Oh," she says, "here it is, *The Parable of the Lamp Under the Bushel*. Okay, I see it. Jesus says: *'The lamp of the body is the eye. Therefore, when your eye is good, your whole body is also full of light; but when it is evil, your body also is full of darkness. Therefore, see whether the light that is in you isn't darkness. If therefore your whole body is full of light, having no part dark, it will be wholly full of light, as when the lamp with its bright shining gives you light.'* So it's saying that good and evil are light and dark."

"Let's break it down. Read it again."

"The lamp of the body is the eye."

"Perception. We are awareness. Go on."

"Therefore, when your eye is good, your whole body is also full of light."

"When awareness is not distorted by ego, you are free from delusion. Next."

"But when it is evil, your body also is full of darkness."

"When the light of full awareness is obscured by ego, then there is darkness, which they're calling evil."

"Therefore, see whether the light that is in you isn't darkness."

"Whether your knowledge isn't false knowledge; delusion, distortion, belief, and so on."

"If therefore your whole body is full of light…"

"Eyes open, clear-eyed."

"…having no part dark…"

"Having no egoic distortion causing us to see what's not and not see what is. It's saying that ego is the source of all evil, which is silly. The view that Brahman is good and Atman is evil would mean that ego is original sin, which makes sense in biblical terms, but words like good and evil and sin are making something wrong that's supposed to be wrong. Ego is of the essence of the dreamstate; without it, there's nothing. You can't make Atman and Maya the bad guys. The parable is an example of the darkness it's describing, which is telling. Read the rest."

"…it will be wholly full of light, as when the lamp with its bright shining gives you light.'"

"Wholly full of light means awake from the dreamstate, enlightenment."

"Wow, seriously?"

"I don't know, but it's interesting. Interpreting the Bible is like submitting a child's finger painting as photographic evidence in a trial, but if we just look at it as myth, as an archetypal story, then provenance doesn't matter, only the fact that it has undergone centuries of filtration and survives in its present form. None of the major religious books can be turned to any serious purpose, but it's fun to think about, so that counts for something."

"So I shouldn't use the bushel stuff?"

"No, I'd say stick with the transition, the apple, that's the key. Like you said, Adam and Eve is a creation myth, we don't have to sweat the details. In the broad strokes, it's very simple. In Genesis 1, God is bored so he creates the dreamstate universe. But God is still bored, so in Genesis

2 and 3, he creates ego, which is the illusion of segregated self. He takes naked Ken and Barbie dolls out of the box and infuses them with the spark of his own awareness along with the capacity for misperception. In short, he creates a set of avatars—a yin mini-me and a yang mini-me—and then hobbles them with emotion."

As I speak, I feel myself warming up to the topic. This is getting surprisingly interesting. I get up and start building a fire as I sort through it.

"Awareness can't miscreate, but it can misperceive. By creating ego, Brahman introduces the appearance of imperfection into his boringly perfect universe. This gives rise to drama and conflict, and now the universe isn't boring anymore, which is the whole point. Who wants to dream a boring dream?"

"That's interesting," Maggie says, "I can use that."

"Sure, since as a filmmaker you're in the same business, projecting something interesting onto a blank screen; appearance for the amusement of awareness; sound and fury, signifying nothing."

"So Adam and Eve were the first characters."

"In the myth, but their motivation is misunderstood. It's not that they become aware of their nakedness and feel shame, it's that they become aware of their meaninglessness and feel fear. That's the real level of their nakedness; being unclothed is just a metaphor. So now we have the source emotion of fear combined with the capacity for misperception which is ego, and the stage of the dramatic universe is set. We have all the pieces needed for our play; theater, stage, characters, passion, ignorance, conflict, and audience. Now the whole thing comes alive and now it's entertaining. Ken and Barbie are animated by the power of fear which hits the imperfect prism of ego and refracts into a full spectrum of emotion."

"Wow," she says, surprised, "that almost makes sense."

"Yeah," I agree, equally surprised, "it almost does."

✷

She makes her notes while I pace in front of the fireplace and try to make sense of things.

"So," I say, "now we can compare this to another creation myth, the big bang, which is also divided into before and after. Before the bang, there was nothing; no space, no time, no energy, no matter, nothing. And then suddenly, *bam!* Genesis. A whole universe springs out of nothing. *Ex nihilo*, something from nothing."

"Isn't the big bang supposed to be science?"

"Religion is a belief system and God is their magical solution. Science is also a belief system and the big bang is *their* magical solution. But what came before God? What came before the big bang? The void, nothingness, the black hole. That's where magic must be summoned, at the exact point where reason fails."

"Yeah, but how can you *not* fail at that point?" she asks thoughtfully. "How can something come out of nothing?"

"Very good. It obviously can't. *Ex nihilo nihil fit*, nothing comes from nothing, meaning the question is wrong. Reason never fails, it only reveals errors in our reasoning. Creation from nothing is effectively disproved, so we have to check our assumptions and start over. No one wants to do that, though, so they resort to magic instead. The big bang and Genesis and other creation myths provide false answers, but when we're really done with the question we won't have answered it, we'll have destroyed it."

"But what happens if we *do* check our assumptions and start over?" she asks. "Don't we come up with the same thing over and over?"

"No. Truth is never hidden and always simple, but you have to ask the right question."

"What's the right question?"

"The right question is always the one that looks like a wall blocking you from going further. Destroy the obstruction and take a step."

"Oh my God, this is way too much for my homework."

"You're helping me with mine now. Keep taking notes, please. The question of how something can come from nothing is false because it assumes the possibility of nothing."

"There can't be nothing?"

"Exactly. Nothing is literally impossible. The proof of one is the disproof of zero. Once you establish the truth of infinite consciousness, you have established the truth of one. If there is one, there is not zero. One is consciousness and consciousness is all."

"So there isn't nothing and there is something?"

"The only something is consciousness. Science and religion resort to magical solutions instead of reason to explain the existence of the physical universe because they are existentially prohibited from acknowledging what has been understood by less obstructed thinkers for many thousands of years. There is no physical universe. Reality is not real."

"Yeah, this is totally your thing now. I don't even know what you just said."

"Okay, so let's get back to your thing. A creation myth doesn't really have to make sense, it just has to be good enough. The reason you don't see angry mobs outside churches and universities demanding less ridiculous stories is because we're all in the same boat. We all have the same black hole inside and we're *all* existentially motivated to go along with the cover-up. That's what these myths do; they help us comfortably ignore these big flashing signs that tell us our stories don't make sense."

"Oh, wait," she says. "A big flashing sign, like, hold on," she digs through her pile of papers. "Okay, *so then God banished Adam and Eve from the Garden of Eden and placed on the east side of the Garden of Eden cherubim and a flaming sword flashing back and forth to guard the way to the tree of life.*"

I stop pacing.

"A flaming sword flashing back and forth?"

"That's what it says."

"That sounds like a railroad crossing, keeping us safely back from danger. That makes sense. Eden is the inner black hole from which we emerge and to which we return, but the whole dramatic element of the dreamstate depends on us not being aware of it. If Ken and Barbie awaken to the fact that they're just hollow plastic dolls, they'll stop performing and the whole thing is over, so that flashing sword is warning them away from truth, away from the realization of meaninglessness, keeping them safely confined within the dramatic production they exist to serve."

"Which is like the stuff you talk about?"

"Maybe. So now we're saying that Eden is the black hole inside everyone, the inner abyss. That's it, really. Eden is the infinite void of featureless consciousness. We appear from the void to participate in the dreamstate, and we return to the void when we're done. We enter through the backstage door, strut and fret our hour upon the stage, and then are heard no more. Eden is the abyss."

"Darn," she says, "that's pretty good."

"No, wait a second," I resume pacing and consider. "Eden is *awareness* of the abyss. To see it is to enter it, no difference, so it's not that we can't *go* there, it's that we're protected from *thinking* it's there. It has to be gated and guarded against our powers of reason. That's the emotional hobbling we mentioned, it keeps us in character. Yeah, that's better."

She takes notes quietly for a minute before asking a question.

"But doesn't that make us something from nothing?"

"No, because we don't exist, which is exactly what awareness of the black hole tells us. No self is true self. The dream of something is not something, it's nothing. There is only consciousness."

"So I don't exist?"

"No, sorry."

"That sucks," she says, taking it well, as well she should. "It says God made Adam from dust, right?"

"Yeah," I say, "ashes to ashes, dust to dust. It's not that Adam and Eve are expelled from paradise, it's that they're born of the void. They emerge from nothingness into the dreamstate where they'll hang out for a while before returning to the nothingness whence they came, right? Eden, black hole, void, singularity, no-self, all the same. That's what they're not supposed to know; not that they're undressed, but that they're unreal."

"And while they're alive there's this cherubim guy with the crazy sword keeping them away from the truth."

"Yes, you can say that's the self-preserving aspect of ego keeping Ken and Barbie from knowing about their fictional nature, which would completely undermine the dramatic production. You can't have everyone breaking out of character or the whole thing falls apart. The human experience must be fully immersive, so an unwilling suspension of disbelief must be imposed on the players."

"Oh, that's my title," she says excitedly. "*The unwilling suspension of disbelief.* I bet Jung and Campbell didn't know any of this stuff. Oh my God, I am *so* getting an A on this!"

✸

What comes from nothing and returns to nothing? Nothing. First, I am nothing, then whatever this is, then nothing again, so the truth of me is nothing. Ask yourself *Who am I?*, and what you'll find is that the source of life isn't a garden, it's a hole. We are animated on a dust-to-dust basis in a dreamstate universe that exists for entertainment purposes only, and the show must go on.

Creatio Ex Nihilo

What exists in truth is the Self alone.
The world, the individual soul and God
are appearances in it.

Ramana Maharshi

ONE BELIEF-BASED OBJECTION to dreamstate-ism is that reality is too complex and huge and just plain *real* not to be real, but this objection is actually a supporting argument inverted. Think of it like a movie. Would it make more sense to actually build working spacecraft, weapons, and deathstars, to hire and outfit a million-clone army, to conduct battle scenes in space, and to blow it all up? Or just to fake it all in a computer?

Through the use of CGI, those ships and characters and battle scenes have no actual existence as we think of actual. They're just an electronic sequence of ones and zeroes arranged by intelligence and desire, and that's what the universe itself actually is, an arrangement of intelligence and desire with no actual actuality. Reality isn't particle-based, it's intelligence-based.

The objection that the universe is just too big and complex *not* to be real actually credits to the dreamstate side of the ledger. It's the physical universe as we think of it that seems unnecessary and unlikely since we have Maya, Goddess of CGI, to do the impossible and create something from nothing: *Creatio ex nihilo.*

❋

"So," Maggie says a few minutes later, "nothing exists as it appears to exist?"

"Or, you could say that everything exists *only* as it appears to exist, but that's very different from saying whatever appears to exist *actually* exists. Remove the unknowable and unprovable, and only consciousness remains."

"But wait," she says, "just saying it's all consciousness doesn't really answer the real question, right? So it's all just the dreamstate, okay, fine, there's no actual universe or anything, but why? What's the point of it all?"

"Okay, remember a few minutes ago when you said something and I said, that's what God said?"

"Yeah, I didn't know what that meant."

"What did you say before that?"

"I don't remember."

"You said your homework project was boring and you wanted to make it interesting."

"Okay," she replies, "so?"

"So that's the point of it all, that's the answer to your question. The key to the story of Adam and Eve is that God was bored with his project and wanted to make it interesting."

She makes a scrunchy face.

"No way."

"Way."

"That's the point of everything? To be interesting?"

"Interesting, entertaining, amusing, of course. What else?"

"To be entertaining for who? Us?"

"For consciousness, Brahman. Awareness and appearance are the black and white of the yin-yang symbol which represents the dreamstate, but it can't just sit there, it has to do something; it has to be set in motion, it has to turn. Appearance can't just exist, it has to be dynamic, spellbinding, enchanting. It must beguile and delight. Brahman must be captivated and transported *into* Atman."

"So when I ask why there's a dreamstate at all, what's the reason for it, your answer is that God was bored and wanted to be entertained?"

"That's it."

"God was bored?"

"Well, we're telling a cartoonish version to put it within our conceptual grasp, but yes. Awareness requires appearance, and appearance can't be boring. In Genesis 1, God creates the heavens and the earth, the universe, right? But obviously, it's still not very interesting. In Genesis 2 and 3 he makes it interesting."

"Is it, though?" she asks, "obvious, I mean? I'm not sure it really sounds that obvious. It actually sounds kind of, uh, dumb."

✿

Maggie sees a lot of different numbers floating around that can add up a lot of different ways. The only number I see is one, and a wisp of vapor shaped like a two. I have gone through the process of cleaning up the universal equation. I have spent years beholding the truth of one and contemplating the appearance of two. I can show my bottom-line and how I got there. I can, with a long list of qualifiers and disclaimers, enlist the support of ancient Eastern teachings and a few Western thinkers too. I can write books about spiritual distillation and the algebraic reduction of personal reality. In the end, however, I can lead people to truth, but I can't make them see. Until we see for ourselves what lies just outside the walls of this magic box, no explanation can ever be more than words. In short, what's obvious to eyes-open me is not visible to eyes-closed Maggie.

And frankly, saying that the apparent universe is just the home entertainment system of infinite consciousness sounds dumb to me too, but the inescapable fact is that meaning is not possible, so any explanation is going to sound dumb. This whole infinite timespace-energymatter universe thing is really just an immersive boob-tube, and if you could ask Brahman why he's glued to it like a fat little couch potato, his answer would be the same as yours or mine: *I don't want to be bored!*

In short, the one and only reason for the dreamstate is

the amusement of awareness. Whether or not you find this explanation satisfying, it is complete and correct and no other explanation is possible. If you want to explain things any other way, you have to enlist belief to do so, meaning that you have to venture back into the dreamstate and construct your argument from the building blocks of make-believe. Happily, there's no reason to collect imaginary puzzle pieces because the ones we have form a clear and complete picture.

Now, take a fresh look at the world from this Brahmanic perspective and marvel at what a magnificent boob-tube it really is. Look around in space and time. Try to appreciate the fantastic diversity of the far-flung dreamstate, not just your tiny corner of it. I may seem to disparage reality because it's not real, but no one can deny that the dreamstate theater is the greatest creation of all. Assuming a hundred billion people living an average of fifty years, that's forty-four quadrillion hours of fantastically diverse entertainment value in the Earth venue alone, and billions more for every one you experience. Not all edge-of-your-seat stuff, of course, but due to the Brahmanic self-limiting feature of Atman, every minute of your life is as fresh and new to Brahman as it is to you, which eliminates the problem of reruns.

✿

If we compiled a list of every explanation for the universe that anyone has ever concocted, including but not limited to God's plan, big bang, evolution of the soul, and great place to catch a roller derby, we'd find that they all collapse under the weight of their own absurdity. Any explanation that assumes the universe actually exists is bound to be goofy. The amusement-of-Brahman explanation may feel a bit anticlimactic because we expect some grand revelation of divine meaning, but no such revelation is possible because no such meaning is possible. The dreamstate universe is meaningless and serves only to amuse the sole beholder personified—you.

✿

Actually, we can go further. We can say with certainty that without appearance there can be no awareness. Conversely, there *is* awareness so there must be something to be aware *of*, even though it has no existence beyond appearance, i.e., a dream. I can say that awareness is true and appearance is untrue, which is true, but I can also personally lay claim to I-Am/Consciousness, which means, technically, that I am qualified to say that appearance does *appear* to exist. Not that it *does* exist, as does the dreamer, nor that it does *not* exist, as doesn't the dreamt, but that it *appears* to exist, like the dream. I can't confirm the content of appearance, but I can confirm the appearance itself. Not what I dream *of*, but *that* I dream.

Descartes' Evil Demon can deceive me about everything except the fact that I exist, of which I am certain because I am aware. That's the difference between everything I believe and the one thing I know, but if the appearances which provide the basis of my self-awareness are illusory, can I still claim them as proof of my existence? Yes. Regardless of what I am aware *of*, I am aware, and as Descartes rightly stated, the Demon can't deceive me about that.

Brahman is perceiver, Atman is the process of perception,

and Maya is the perceived. Perceiver, perception and perceived are not three but one; consciousness. Consciousness, being one without other, can only be conscious of itself, like a mirror reflecting itself in a void, creating from nothing the appearance of everything; *creatio ex nihilo*. So, based on the certain fact that there is only consciousness, we can conclude that the dreamstate universe is, essentially, an infinity mirror.

So that's nice.

✳

Are you having fun with all this dreamstate stuff? I hope so since that's really all it's good for. We're just making mud pies and smashing sandcastles, so we might as well enjoy it. We can never really reconcile appearances any more than we can reconcile dreams or memories or feelings. In the end, we're left to accept the fact that the dreamstate is what it is, even though it's not.

If you went up to one of your scientist buddies and told him the moon landings were a hoax, he'd laugh at you, but based on what? Did he sit down for several months and make a complete review of the facts? Did he study all the evidence on both sides? Did he subject himself to a rigorous emotional purification to render himself qualified to judge? Did he conduct a methodical inquiry that would stand up to global peer review? No. Has he ever even given the matter a moment's thought? Of course not, he's just married to the narrative like the rest of the herd, and to him, you're just a conspiracy nutjob. Sure, he'll sneer at your stupidity, not because he's the rational Spock to your goofball McCoy as he'd like to believe, but because he's an eyes-shut child wrapped in the dogmatic security blanket of a herd from which you are a defector-in-training. Your scientist pal is not open-minded, questioning, welcoming of new information, or operating from any sense of curiosity or wonder, he's just another cow.

This is why I like to stress the understanding of developmental age over physical age. Once you determine a person's real age, they will appear to you as simple and transparent as an actual child. This applies to pretty much everyone, so unless someone is exuding some weird detachment, you can safely assume they're stuck at a pre-pubescent stage of development. It looks a little funky when you start seeing people's true age accurately, but this internal growth regulator is not the imperfection it might seem. Adults simply aren't amusing, so the only way to keep the dreamstate fun is to keep it young.

Now, try to see your entrenched science friend as an aspect of yourself. See how you react to things reflexively that might deserve a closer look. Not that you should look into those things, but that you should look into that reflexive reaction. If you want to make a journey, you have to get up and move, and you do it by opening your eyes and looking. Looking and seeing are what it all comes down to, not level of understanding or state of consciousness or depth of compassion. If you just want to be content, whatever, but if you want to wake up, you have to open your eyes.

I, who probably shouldn't be allowed to cross busy streets unattended, have rendered unto dust the three great empires of thought—science, religion, and philosophy—with no more effort than takes to melt a snowflake. That's not a reflection on my awesomeness (nor lack thereof), but on how appallingly naked our idiot-emperors truly are. Here in our Dreamstate Wonderland, the rabbit-hole is reality and solid footing is the illusion. I-Am/Consciousness is knowledge and everything else is belief. We mistake describing for understanding, but nothing that's not completely understood is understood at all, and nothing can be completely understood because nothing, including knowledge, is real. Ask your scientist friend what matter is made of, or what time is, or life or space or anything, and watch him start to dance. Who's the conspiracy whacko now? The secret of the dreamstate is not to look, but you can if you want to; you just have to open your eyes.

✸

"The one creation myth that contains all others," I tell Maggie, "is that creation is not a myth. Once you accept creation as fact, you've already wandered off into the weeds."

"You're supposed to say spoiler alert first."

"Sorry."

"Is there a creation myth you like better than Adam and Eve?" she asks as she collects her stuff and prepares to leave.

"There's one that says Brahman was bored so he created Maya to amuse him. Maya then told Brahman to make a universe and stock it with people. Then she cut Brahman up into billions of pieces and hid one piece in each person, and ever since then they have been playing a game of hide-and-seek, people trying to find Brahman and Maya trying to stop them."

"Oh," she pauses and stares into space for a moment. "Does that make any sense?"

"It's okay as these things go."

"Well," she asserts, "if you don't like anyone else's, maybe you should come up with your own."

"Well," I say, "maybe I will."

The Myth of Creation

MYTHOLOGY, *n*. The body of a primitive people's beliefs
concerning its origin, early history, heroes, deities and so
forth, as distinguished from the true accounts which it
invents later.

Ambrose Bierce

O NCE UPON A TIME, before the birth of time, there
existed a Great Beholder. Not only was he a *great*
beholder, he was the *only* beholder.

The Great Beholder could see everything forever in all
directions which would have made him very happy had there
been anything to see, but in all directions, there was Nothing
Forever. The Great Beholder was Pure Awareness, but there
was nothing to be aware *of*.

This made the Great Beholder very sad.

☼

The Great Beholder had two qualities that seemed like they were very *good* qualities, but they were actually very *bad* qualities. They were very *bad* because they made the Great Beholder very *sad*.

The first of these two qualities was Infinite Infinitude. Because the Great Beholder was *everything*, there was nothing *other* than him, so he could never have a friend to play with or a dark place to explore.

The second of these two qualities was Perfect Perfection. Because the Great Beholder was incapable of error, there could never be anything different or unexpected, so he could never experience Surprise & Delight.

✿

Then, one day, the Great Beholder had an idea! *(This would have been the very first idea ever if there really was such a thing as time, but time is just an idea, so everything really happens at once which is not a problem because nothing really happens at all. Can you imagine if you had to do everything at once? Thank you, Time!)*

"I am the Great Beholder," he thought, "but there is nothing to *behold*. I am Pure Awareness, but there is nothing to be aware *of*. There is only me so there's nothing to see, but maybe I could *imagine* something else!"

And thus was born the Illusion of Appearance.

✿

So he did! The Great Beholder said, "Let there be Something Else," and there was Something Else! And he looked upon it and saw that it was good. Now there was both a Beholder and a Beheld, and although the Beheld was only in the Great Beholder's imagination, it was *way* better than nothing.

Of course, there could never *really* be Something Else because the Great Beholder was Infinitely Infinite, but now there was the *dream* of Something Else, and the Great Beholder had the appearance of Otherness to be aware of.

And thus was born the Illusion of Two.

✿

Then, one day, the Great Beholder had *another* idea. *(For what else was there for him to do but sit around and have ideas all day?)*

"I think I'll imagine a whole *bunch* of Something Else," he thought, "and then I won't be bored anymore!"

So the Great Beholder imagined an infinite universe and he filled it with all manner of Something Else like planets and stars and rivers and trees and animals. And he called it his Imaginary Playground.

And thus was born the Illusion of Timespace,
Energymatter, Duality, Causality, and Life.

✿

But the Great Beholder was *still* sad because he was *still* bored because his Imaginary Playground was Perfectly Perfect, so there was never any *im*perfection. Everything always made Perfect Sense, which was perfectly dull.

The Great Beholder watched galaxies and planets spinning

around, but that only made him dizzy. Then he watched animals running around and eating and making more animals, but that only made him sleepy.

Everything in the Imaginary Playground worked *exactly* as it was supposed to *all* of the time, so how could the Great Beholder ever feel Surprise & Delight?

He couldn't. So he was still bored. So he was still sad.

✺

Then, one day, the Great Beholder had *another* idea.

"Maybe I can imagine the Imaginary Playground so it *isn't* perfect," he thought. "If everything didn't always make Perfect Sense, then it would be able to Surprise & Delight me!"

But sadly, because he was Perfectly Perfect, the Great Beholder could not imagine Imperfection, so he was still sad.

✺

Then, one day, the Great Beholder had *another* idea.

"Maybe," he thought, "I might enjoy my Imaginary Playground if I could play *in* it instead of just looking *at* it!"

But gosh, he wondered, how?

"I can't imagine anything *more* than perfect, and I can't imagine anything *less* than perfect," he reasoned, "but maybe I can imagine someone who can!"

So the Great Beholder imagined a finite version of himself, a *Little* Beholder, and placed it in his Imaginary Playground.

And thus was born the Illusion of Self.

✿

But alas, the Little Beholder knew he was really the Great Beholder, so he knew everything about everything and he was still bored so he was still sad.

"What's the point of having an Imaginary Playground and a Little Beholder if I still can't be Surprised & Delighted?" the Great Beholder asked himself.

"No point," he answered.

"No point *whatsoever*," he added for emphasis.

✿

Then, one day, the Great Beholder had *another* idea.

"Maybe," he thought, "I could pluck out the memory of the Little Beholder, who is really just me, and then I could explore the Imaginary Playground without knowing who I really am. I could tie a blindfold around the Little Beholder's brain, and then I could experience Surprise & Delight!"

And *lo!* It worked! The Little Beholder walked around and played and explored, and everything was a source of Surprise & Delight and a lion ate him.

And thus was born the Illusion of Ignorance.

✿

So now, the Great Beholder imagined *many* Little Beholders and sprinkled them throughout his Imaginary Playground, and he plucked out their memories and blindfolded their brains so they couldn't remember who they really were or know what was really going on. Where that memory had been, there was now a scary hole which made the Little

Beholders tremble with Terrible Dread and look away.

And thus was born the Illusion of Emotion.

✣

So now, the Great Beholder had solved the two problems that caused him to feel boredom and sadness.

One problem that caused the Great Beholder's boredom and sadness was his Perfect Perfection. For the Great Beholder, everything must always make Perfect Sense. One plus one must always equal two. One plus one could never equal three or thirty-three or a slice of pie.

But for the *Little* Beholders, it was different. The *Great* Beholder was Perfectly Perfect and couldn't make the Imaginary Playground *im*perfect, but he could make the Little Beholders *behold it* imperfectly. Imperfection could not lie in the *Beheld*, but it *could* lie in the eye of the *Beholder*.

One plus one must always equal two, but the Great Beholder could jigger and boggle the Little Beholders so they would believe it equaled three or thirty-three or a slice of pie.

Of course, the Little Beholders were really Pure Awareness like the Great Beholder, but because they were Imaginary Creatures, they could have their awareness distorted, contorted, befuddled, bamboozled, twisty-turned and just plain higgledy-piggledy gobbledy-gooked.

And thus was born the Illusion of Non-Sense.

✣

The *other* problem that caused the Great Beholder's sadness and boredom was that he was Infinitely Infinite. He *saw* everything and *knew* everything and *was* everything, so he could never be Surprised and Delighted.

But for the Little Beholders, it was different. The *Great* Beholder could not be finite, but the *Little* Beholders *could*. They could have a beginning and a middle and an end. They could be *here* but not *there*, *now* but not *then*, *this* but not *that*. The Little Beholders were really infinite like the Great Beholder because they really *were* the Great Beholder, but because they were *imagined*, they could be imagined in tiny polarized units that could attract and repel each other.

> *And thus was born the Illusion of*
> *Harmony and Conflict.*

❀

So now, there were many Little Beholders at play in the Imaginary Playground of the Great Beholder, all having their own adventures. And even though none of them knew it, they were all really the Great Beholder incognito, so all of *their* adventures were really *his* adventures.

"And now I have many friends," the Great Beholder exclaimed, "and I'll never be lonely again!"

> *And thus was born the Illusion of Connection.*

❀

It was like having a Super-Duper Television with billions of channels that he could watch all at once, and he could be the star of every show and experience all the drama and conflict and comedy and tragedy. He could be silly and non-sensical and wise and foolish and crazy and clever and all the wonderful things he could never be on his own.

"Oh, joy!" cried the Great Beholder. "Now I will never be bored again! Now I can laugh and sing and dance and play! I can commit acts of heroism and cowardice, kindness and brutality! I can create and procreate and co-create and miscreate! I can believe in clever lies and silly truths! I can be wrong and ignorant and scared and mean! I can be villain and hero, madman and saint, criminal and victim, peasant and king! I can create magnificent cities and smash them to bits! I can experience pleasure and pain and all the emotions; agony no less than elation, suffering no less than joy, hatred no less than love, but let's go easy on peace and contentment because that's pretty boring and seriously, what's the point, right?"

✿

And this is how the Great Beholder overcame the curious problems of Perfect Perfection and Infinite Infinitude. And now the Great Beholder is so happy that he wants to clap his hands together, but the only hands he has to clap with are *yours*, so now, Great Beholder, clap your hands together in Surprise & Delight!

In Praise of Bullshit

> If you stand right fronting and face to face to a fact, you
> will see the sun glimmer on both its surfaces, as if it were a
> scimitar, and feel its sweet edge dividing you through the
> heart and marrow, and so you will happily conclude your
> mortal career. Be it life or death, we crave only reality. If we
> are really dying, let us hear the rattle in our throats and
> feel cold in the extremities; if we are alive, let us go about
> our business.

Henry David Thoreau

T HOREAU WAS WRONG. Actually, most of the historical thinkers I like best were around 99% wrong, but 1% right is a solid A on the human bell curve. By reality, Thoreau meant truth, which no one craves. Even Thoreau didn't crave truth, he just had a mild aversion to bullshit, which is hardly the same thing. Everyone has a bullshit limit beyond which it can be too much, but that's just a matter of comfort level and doesn't make you a truth-nut.

✿

There's no point in pointing out that the government is Orwellian or society is Orwellian because *everything* is Orwellian. Everyone you see is wearing a mask and all you have to do to see the grumpy old man behind the ho-ho-ho-ing Santa is yank off his beard. Diogenes searches for an honest man but can't find one because all men are intrinsically dishonest, including the man in search of an honest man.

It takes a complex energetic process to see what's not and not see what is. The energy is emotion and the process is doublethink. Doublethink is not something we do here and there, now and then, but everywhere, all the time. Even to say that we are characters on a stage is to conceal from ourselves the fact that there is no stage and that we are playing out our little fantasies all alone in the barren vastness of nothing forever, and even *that* is still bullshit.

✿

As a practical necessity, we all suspend disbelief all the time. Somewhere inside you know that your fast food lunch is more noxious than nutritious. You might as well spread lard on a pack of cigarettes and eat that, but you eat it anyway because, seriously, it's not just lunch that's so damn crazy, it's everything. Where do you draw the line? You would never be able to eat in a restaurant or from a grocery store if you couldn't bullshit yourself about the quality, safety and sourcing of the food. My doctor cares about my health, my priest cares about my soul, my bank cares about my financial well-being, this restaurant isn't cutting corners, my friends and family don't talk about me the way I talk about them, politicians work for the people, religions care about truth, the justice system cares about justice, the healthcare system cares about health, reporters are fair and balanced, this adult can be trusted with my kids, that cop wakes up every morning and performs a rigorous moral inventory, infatuation is love, organic produce is safe, these pills will make me better, I am not a number, my life has meaning, my opinion matters, my vote counts, I will live on through my children, I will be remembered, I am special, I am real, I matter... and on and on and on. You have to bullshit yourself about everything just to get through the day. It's the spoonful of sugar that helps the reality go down.

Probably the only thing you can ever really trust in life is your parents, and you sure as hell can't trust them. You can trust them to have your best interests at heart and to want what's best for you, but what does that mean? It means eat your veggies, do your homework, take your medicine, get good grades, go to church, go to college, get a job, get married, have some babies and do unto your kids as we have done unto you. In short, mom and dad are fully indoctrinated and consider it their job to indoctrinate you too. Welcome to the machine.

✾

Jeremiah Johnson wasn't a nature-lover, he was a bullshit-hater, and a lonely, brutal mountain-life was his only alternative to a bullshit life. He might have preferred the tropical island in *Cast Away* that Chuck Noland was so eager to get away from, or maybe, like Chuck, he would have realized that at least *some* human contact was required to maintain sanity. Semi-reclusive mountain life is one thing, but alone on an island is the earthly equivalent of nothing forever. That's *zero* bullshit, and that's not what *any*one wants.

Chuck Noland finds himself *too* alone so he has to create Wilson. Wilson isn't just a cinematic sidekick device that allows Chuck to voice his thoughts, it's a human companion device that allows the character to make at least one emotional connection. A human relationship doesn't have to be with a human, but it does have to *be*. By making just one connection, one becomes connected. We don't have to be *very* connected, but we can't be *dis*connected. We need an audience to validate our performance, and it can be a bloody volleyball as long as we can make ourselves believe in it and feel beheld. As long as we feel beheld, we feel real. Without at least one emotional lifeline tethering us to the dreamstate, it would have no emotional dimension and neither, therefore, would we. Stranded on a desert island surrounded by nothing forever is everyone's *real* reality, but we must remain ignorant of this truth at any cost, and we do this by making emotional connections which are so illusory and one-sided that, in a pinch, an inanimate object will suffice. The connection between a mother and her child may seem more real than the one between Chuck and Wilson, but it's not more true. All connection is illusion. As long as we feel connected, we are.

I myself am comfortable with very little human contact, but not with none. It's not from loneliness or desire, but from a need to maintain a vestige of the illusion that I am here and real. What are you, my imagined reader, except a bloody volleyball for whom I perform? You are my purpose, my context. I spend a good part of my waking hours in some form of dialog with you and you are an essential part of my life. You are my Wilson; you're a good listener, not a big talker, and you laugh at all my jokes, which is just how I like you.

What are television and radio but electronic Wilsons? What is social media but the appearance of connection? We don't need an actual physical person to interact with when a graphic user interface will do. We believe there's a human on the other end and maybe there is, but maybe there's not. Who cares? It doesn't matter what we connect with as long as we feel connected. Maybe in a few years, human contact will be rendered obsolete by a global AI companion program called Wilson, and in another few years we won't have to leave our room because Wilson will project reality onto the walls, and then directly into our brains as we spend our lives floating in jars. Or maybe this happened eons ago and that's where we are right now, merely dreaming we're not. What's the difference between believing that you're sitting in an opulent restaurant eating a steak, and believing that you're sitting in a subterranean warzone eating a bowl of milky snot? Hell if I know, but I'll have the steak.

✧

Why does a renunciate go off to live in a mountaintop cell? To try to get away from the bullshit that coats everything. Why does he take a vow of silence? To shut down the internal bullshit factory so he doesn't have to puff out clouds of oily black smoke every time he encounters a fellow being. What does Jeremiah Johnson mean when he scornfully states, "I've been to a town"? He means that the whole reason for his harsh, solitary existence is to get away from bullshit. What does Thoreau mean by "the mud and slush of opinion, and prejudice, and tradition, and delusion, and appearance, that alluvion which covers the globe"?

He means bullshit.

We can never become bullshit-free because bullshit is the medium of the dreamstate, and we're not just *in* it, we *are* it. You can skim the scum off a pond, but if you skim off the water it's not a pond anymore, it's just an empty hole. In other words, seeking to be bullshit-free is just more bullshit.

✧

Would you participate in group suicide so you could catch a ride to heaven on a spaceship hidden behind a passing comet? Do you agree with theologians who believe the amputated foreskin of Jesus ascended into heaven with him and became the rings of Saturn? Do you believe that dark-skinned people are cursed by God but can become "white and delightsome" if they become more valiant?

Do you believe that seventy-five million years ago there was a galactic ruler who oversaw seventy-six planets including Earth, and to reduce overpopulation on his planets the ruler called the people in for tax audits, but instead, injected them with a paralyzing agent and then flew them to Earth and stacked them around volcanoes in which he detonated hydrogen bombs and killed them all? And that the galactic ruler then set up traps like electronic fly paper to catch the billions of blown-up souls floating around, and then brought them to special cinemas and showed them training films?

Do you wear sacred underwear that protects you from fire, bullets, disease and death? Do you believe in swinging a chicken around your head to absorb your sins, then killing it and feeding it to the poor? Do you forsake clothing and only own a peacock feather and a water gourd?

Do you believe that wearing yellow should be forbidden, that yawning is satanic, that all dogs should be killed, and that anyone who doesn't share your beliefs should be forced to drink boiling water, be burned, branded, dismembered, crucified and condemned to hell?

We believe that we are rational beings who can scoff at those less rational than ourselves, but what if we ask what if? What if we're *not* rational? What if delusion lies *prior* to perception? What if we are somehow defective or deceived in our understanding? What if we're under a sleep spell that tells us we're awake? Your worldview is completely sense-based, but what if the evidence of your senses was ruled inadmissible? Then your entire case for the existence of the universe would be thrown out, and bullet-proof underwear and the resurrection of the Holy Prepuce would make as much sense as anything else. It's not the bullshit that we believe that holds us in dreamstate stasis, it's the bullshit we never question.

❉

No man is an island, entire of itself. Each is a piece of the continent, a part of the main. If a clod be washed away by the sea, Europe is the less. Each man's death diminishes me, for I am involved in mankind. Therefore, send not to know for whom the bell tolls, it tolls for thee.

-John Donne

To be is to be alone. Every man *is* an island entire of itself, and no amount of Wilsons can change that. The lie is that the bell tolls for thee, but when it actually does you won't actually hear it because you'll actually be dead. Therefore, go ahead and send to know for whom the bell tolls, it tolls for some other poor schmuck.

The Uncanny Valley

> Now I believe I can hear the philosophers protesting that
> it can only be misery to live in folly, illusion, deception and
> ignorance, but it isn't — it's human.
>
> *Desiderius Erasmus, 1466-1536*

A COURSE IN MIRACLES says nothing real can be threatened and nothing unreal exists. The *Bhagavad Gita* says the unreal never is and the real never is not. In both instances, the word real is relative where an absolute is required, so we modify the statements thusly: "Nothing *true* can be threatened. Nothing *untrue* exists." and, "The *untrue* never is. The *true* never is not." Now both statements are correct.

Truth is. Untruth ain't.

✿

Brahman is awareness, Maya is appearance. Brahman is simple, Maya is anything but. Scholars and sages struggle to understand Maya and generally conclude that her palace of illusion, the dreamstate, is both real and unreal. This is perfectly correct as long we agree that the words real and unreal don't really mean anything.

The question is, is reality real? By saying that it's both real and unreal, scholars and sages are pandering to their constituents. They don't want to go out and get real jobs, but if they go around saying reality isn't real, their followers are going to fire them and hire some new scholars and sages who don't say a lot of stupid shit. I myself don't mind saying a lot of stupid shit, so I'll go ahead and answer the question.

Reality must be *real* since it's in the name, but reality is not *true*. There is no truality. Reality is subjectively real and truth is objectively true. We can say the universe is both real and unreal, but we can't say it's both true and untrue. It's not. In fact, we can definitively say the universe is *un*true, just as we can definitively say that untruth does not exist. The dreamstate may be real, but it's not true. It may *seem* to exist, but it knowably does not.

✿

Holy smoke! See what we did there? We gave a simple answer to a simple question! Let's lock it in. *If* truth is unchanging, *and* reality changes, *then* reality is untrue. That works, let's do another. *If* untruth does not exist, *and* reality is untrue, *then* reality does not exist. Yep, they both work. Saying reality isn't real may be stupid shit, but it's *true* stupid shit.

Gosh, I'm pretty good at this scholar and sage stuff. I should be granted three wishes! Okay, one, I wish that wishes were horses so beggars could ride, or at least eat. Two, I wish that *Berlinisches Polytechnikum* would confer upon me an honorary doctorate in philosophy which I would dispatch a supermodel to decline on my behalf and deliver a protest speech protesting protest speeches. Three, I wish that all universities would shut down their philosophy departments and channel the funding into AI research so robots can wipe out humanity while I'm still young enough to enjoy it.

※

Maya is easily understood when we realize there is no Maya. This is the real-but-not-true dichotomy, and no one can wrap their heads it because it's too counter-intuitive, counter-sensible, counter-obvious, and just plain counter-*everything* to believe. How can reality not be true? If it's real then it must be true, but if it's not true then it can't be real, right? We can't grasp the untruth of reality because there's nothing to grasp; there's no *there* there. As with a dream, you can observe, participate and interpret, but not understand.

Erasmus reckoned our passion-to-reason ratio at twenty-four to one, with reason confined to a cramped corner of the head and the rest of the body governed by passions. That's why, however much you might be on board with this dream-state stuff, as soon as you look up from this book you will be fully re-intoxicated by the reality of reality. Rightly so, since reality *is* real, and there's no point in pretending it's not.

Scholars and sages describing Maya will resort to words like ineffable, enigmatic and inscrutable, but these are just different ways of saying what they should just say in the first place which is that we can't grasp Maya because there's no Maya to grasp. She doesn't exist. Don't try telling *her* that, though. She may not exist, but you're living in her house and, believe me, her sense of humor is very different from yours.

Whatever else Maya may be, she is not random. She is subject to inviolable rules that we are able to see as pattern, experience as energetic flow, and understand as the mechanical structure of the dreamstate. At the level of outward appearance we experience ourselves as drops in the ocean, but at the underlying structural level, drop and ocean are unmistakably one. Once you've opened your eyes and had time to adjust, that unified underlayment becomes more visible, navigable and real than surface appearances. The tradeoff is that once you've wandered into the service tunnels below—the mechanical underside where the story ends and the costumes come off—the magic kingdom above loses its luster and your connection with the still-enchanted folk up there will span a divide only visible to you. In short, you will have become an adult in a place designed for children.

It's a small world after all.

✿

I understand pattern as energetic flow to which I am subtly attuned and with which I interact. This mode of heightened function is not the sole domain of the Integrated State, but my experience is that it works far more effectively, consistently, and seamlessly once the segregating influence of wrong-knowing has been eliminated. Ego isolates us from integrated awareness like a blindfold keeping us in the dark on a sunny day. Once the benighting mask of ego is discarded, whole new ways of perceiving, knowing and behaving open up and reality as you currently experience it will be remembered only as a twilight state of pre-emergence.

In the Integrated State, right-knowing, right-action and right-wanting become as natural as seeing, hearing and balance, and no more or less miraculous. We can think of this right-being as the spiritual sense. People in whom the spiritual sense is not yet awakened seem only half-born, like drunken toddlers at best, or grunting mutants at not-so best.

In the field of AI there's a phenomenon called the uncanny valley. It refers to a line on a graph that trends upward as it depicts the increasing level of comfort we feel toward a robot the more human it appears. The line goes steadily up until the robot gets *too* human, *too* eerily real, and then the line dips dramatically—the uncanny valley—as observer comfort turns to confusion and revulsion. So close yet so far. This is how someone in whom the spiritual sense is not awakened appears to one in whom it is; eerily human, but somehow not. And not just someone, everyone.

Maybe some archetypal commonality explains why we picture sleepwalkers, monsters, and zombies in the same eyes-closed, arms-extended pose, plodding blindly along, alive but incoherent. What if you woke up and found that everyone looks like that? What if Adventureland is really Zombieland? What if the zombie apocalypse already happened and we lost? What if you're a zombie right now, and believing you're not is just one of the symptoms? What if the *real* Original Sin is segregation and the *real* Fall of Man is not from grace but lucidity? And if you found out, would you want to get back to the boring-ass garden? Or would you decide that being a zombie isn't the problem you need to fix, it's being awake?

Fun stuff.

✿

Those glasses you wear to watch a 3D movie distort your perception, but they make the 3D movie make sense. You can take them off, but then the screen blurs and you are basically unplugged from the dramatic event you're attending. Now you're the one theater patron who is not entranced, but what's the point of going to the theater except to be entranced? So now you can wander around and look down on all the other moviegoers still "chained" to their seats, still plugged into their fictional universe. Now you can explore the theater, see where the toilet paper and urinal cakes are stored, swipe some Gummy Bears, make a study of all the mundane details that go into running a cineplex, totally own the place, but what you can't do now is enjoy the movie, which is the only reason to be in a theater in the first place. That was your life up there on the screen; your people, your context, your drama. Now, for better and worse, you don't have any of that anymore, so you have to figure out what you *do* have. This is what it means to be lucid in a place designed to immerse you in the sub-lucid experience. The price of waking up is being solid in a ghost world. You hear sound and detect movement, but the reality in which everyone else is absorbed is now just a vague abstraction to you. You try returning to your seat and putting the glasses back on, but that bubble can't be unpopped.

"It's not real," you remind yourself, "the movie is not reality." But you're wrong. The people and the movie *are* real because that's what reality *is*, and the only alternative is a dark, empty room. In the Integrated State, you're still in the theater with the audience, but you're no longer one of them. *In* the world but not *of* the world really means *in* the theater, but not *of* the dramatic event. Is that what you want? I'm just playing devil's advocate here, but what's the point? This whole thing gets billed as a spiritual journey but it's really something else, so it makes sense to pause now and then and ask yourself if where you're going is where you really want to be.

❖

The truth of you lies at the center of your being like the singularity at the center of your universe. Your universe is yours alone and revolves around the zero-point of your awareness. By undergoing ego-loss and arriving at singularity, the unity of self and nonself is revealed, leaving you free to participate in the shaping and co-creation of your personal reality. Awareness is unchanged, but the distorting ego-lens barrier has been removed so you're confronted with an altered version of reality in which everything looks similar but works differently.

But there's a price. By removing the ego-lens you are removing the third-dimension of the dreamstate, in the same way that taking off your 3D glasses detaches you from a 3D movie. But the movie is the whole point of the theater in the first place. It may not be true, but it is pretty amusing, and by detaching from your character you're detaching from your life. It's not a good or bad thing, but it's definitely a thing. By removing the magic lens of ego, you are draining the world of its emotional depth and color. The price of truth is illusion, but illusion is the essence of the dreamstate and the dreamstate is your home. Why would you want to break the spell of meaning and awaken to the reality of an empty box? Yes, you are the totality, like Brahman, but also like Brahman, you are hard to please. Reckoned thusly, all this undoing of chains and opening of eyes and taking of red pills suddenly looks rather self-defeating, and what's the point of defeating yourself? Cui bono?

✿

The spiritual journey is not a process of heart-centric self-unfolding but of heartless self-annihilation. You must arise phoenix-like from the corpse of your character. If you want to know the true essence of something, *any*thing, you must destroy it to the utmost of your power and see what remains. If anything *does* remain, you're not done. This pro-cess of self-distillation is really the only spiritual practice that leads to awakening, all others being meant to accomplish the opposite. Destroy ego and wake up *in* the dreamstate, destroy the dreamstate and awaken *from* it. Nothing in the universe of appearance is solid, nothing has substance, so nothing survives the distillation process except awareness itself. No matter what you start with, all that ever remains is consciousness. This is where the word *spirit* actually makes sense. Spirit is the end product of the distillation process, and no distillation process is ever complete until nothing but pure spirit remains.

✿

My biased view is that the Integrated State is the one goal of all human spirituality, growth and ambition. It must be the direction of travel for anyone in the Segregated State because there's nowhere else to go. A chick in the egg only has two choices; stay in or break out. You can either stay in the zone of neutral buoyancy or smash out of your comfort zone and into a lonelier but more expansive experience of the dreamstate and, perhaps, beyond.

But my unbiased view is that my biased view is incorrect. Any way you cut it, there's nowhere to go, so anywhere is as good as anywhere else. You can kill the Buddha and slay ego, but you can't put a dent in Brahman, so you might as well go where you feel like going and do what you feel like doing. Do what thou wilt, follow your stupid bliss, why not? By what better star might you navigate?

The Great Puzzle

How queer everything is to-day! And yesterday things went on just as usual. I wonder if I've been changed in the night? Let me think: was I the same when I got up this morning? I almost think I can remember feeling a little different. But if I'm not the same, the next question is, Who in the world am I? Ah, that's the great puzzle!

Alice, Lewis Carroll

I HAVE DRIFTED OFF INTO A LIGHT DOZE while working but awaken to a knock at the door. "What fresh hell is this?" I plagiarize again and yell come in again, expecting Maggie this time. Who else but her or Lisa way up here? But it's neither of them.

She comes in, looks around briefly, and walks to the table where I'm sitting by candlelight. She pulls a pack of filterless cigarettes from one of her puffy sleeves and lights up. She blows the match out in a stream of smoke and tosses it on the floor. I'm surprised that I'm not more surprised to see her.

"Can I get you something?" I ask. "Wine?"

"I'm a seven and a half year-old girl, pervert."

"Well, you seem very grown up for a seven and a half year-old girl." I say in what seems like a child-appropriate tone.

"Cut the baby talk, Chester. I'm old enough to be your great-great-grandmother."

"Ooh," I say, "*vampire.*"

"Don't start with that shit. I'm in no mood."

She climbs up onto the chair across from me.

"What *are* you in the mood for?" I ask.

"Got any drugs? Hook a sister up?"

"Drugs? Uh, not really. Maybe some aspirin."

"Jesus, some epidemic."

She hops out of the chair and walks to the fireplace.

"I'm not totally sure what's going on here," I say.

"It's pretty simple," she explains. "To you, I'm a character you're stealing, right?"

"Well, *re-imagining,* I would say…"

"And to me, you're a character in my dream who thinks he's writing me, obviously."

"Obviously. And how do we know who's right?"

"There is no *right*. Believe me, I've looked. Everything is relative; damnably, infuriatingly, hackles-raisingly, blood-boilingly relative."

"My, what big words you know."

"Zip it, assface. I've been banging around inside this puzzle box for a century and a half wearing a goddamn *pinafore* for chrissakes. Have you ever worn a goddamn *pinafore*?"

"I have not."

"It gets old."

"But you're *Alice!* You're beloved by children of all ages."

"That's what I tell the clerk when I go in for a pack of butts and a fifth of Cutty. Doesn't help."

"You're not what I expected."

"If you think you're writing me, write me different."

"Like how?"

"Get me into some street clothes for starters. Make me eighteen and really hot."

"It doesn't work like that, you just come out the way you come out. You're Alice. You're seven and a half and you wear a pinafore."

"And talk like a sailor and smoke like a chimney?"

"Yeah, I'm not sure where that's coming from."

"So, not so much author as scribe."

"I've often said as much. Can you dream me different?"

"Maybe I already am and you don't know it."

"Good point from your perspective."

"It's the only one I got."

"Can you make me say something weird?"

"I'd rather make you say something interesting."

She sits on the chair next to the fireplace, puts her feet up on the hearth and stares into the flames.

"Morpheus wasn't any help?" I ask.

"The black Humpty-Dumpty? Goes up one little level and thinks he's the master of reality? No, not a big help."

"Well, he's just a fictional character, you know."

She stares at me for a long moment, then shakes her head.

"How long have you been doing this?" she asks.

"This? Oh, nearly thirty years, I suppose."

"Jesus," she snorts, "you've got the brain of a child."

"Don't tell the police," I reply.

"Oh," she says after a pause, "the constabulary, yes. Very droll."

"Tough crowd. Winnie-the-Pooh would have laughed."

"Yeah, like he laughed when I kicked the stuffing out of him for getting his head stuck in my honeypot."

"Jesus, too much information."

I pick up my glass and move to the hearth.

"When I leave here," she says, "you'll cease to exist, you know—*bang!*—just like a candle."

"And when I stop writing—*poof!*—no more you."

"If only."

I consider my response but I don't have one. I take a sip from my glass.

"Yeah, drink some more wine," she says, "that's really working for you."

"Snotty little brat, aren't you?"

"Comes with the territory," she sniffs and spits a bit of tobacco into the flames.

"Maybe it's Mr. Carroll you should be snotty with," I suggest.

"Charles? Do you not know he's dead?"

"Well, yeah, but…"

"Do you not *get* that I'm trapped in a dream? Do you not *get* that I can do *anything* but change *nothing*? I can bring Uncle Charles in right now and waltz him with your dog, but it's all just a dream! Do you not *get* that?"

"Sure, and I can have you hop up on the table and…"

"*Careful*, I'm beloved."

"…and dance a jig and sing a bawdy ditty."

"But can you? Really? Can you really have me do that? Can you sit at your machine and write me that way?"

"Well, no, probably not."

"And I can't make Uncle Charles even *appear* to appear, so what good is any of it? I'm not the dreamer of my dream and you're not the author of your book. As clever as we may be—as *lucid*, as you say—we're both still stuck in this infernal box."

"You think that's true?"

"*Nothing* is true," she snaps churlishly.

"Didn't Hitler said that?"

"Don't throw the baby out with the bathwater," she replies, popping out a train of smoke rings, each tunneling gracefully through the last.

"Go ahead, say it," she says, flicking her ash on the floor.

"Say what?"

"Vyasa, Krishna. Spit it out."

"You're in my head?"

"Any you're in mine. Or maybe there's just one head and we're both in it. Who knows, who cares. Go ahead with your stupid thing."

"Well, at the start of *The Mahabharata*, the version…"

"Yeah, yeah, the version you prefer. So Krishna is the creator of the universe they're both in, but Vyasa is the author of the poem they're both in, so when they get together they ponder which of them is creating the other. That about right?"

"Good enough."

"Two snakes eating each other's tails?"

"Or birthing each other, I suppose."

"Gross. I went through all this with the Red King and those Tweedle-tards. You'd think there'd be an end to it at some point."

"Infinity mirror."

She thinks about that.

"Yeah, okay, so I didn't go *through* the looking glass, I just went *into* it, and everything since then has just been my mind bouncing back and forth?"

"Flag doesn't move, wind doesn't move, mind doesn't move.

What moves?"

She rubs her little eyes with her little fingers and groans.

"That Zen shit gives me a headache. Why is a raven like a writing desk? Because they're both highly flammable. What's so hard about that?"

She rolls up on one side to scratch her ass on the other. She flicks her cigarette at the fireplace, missing by a mere fourteen feet.

"Okay," she says, lighting another cigarette, "wine."

"Uh, I'm not sure that's a good…"

"You're in my head, I'm on your page. What's the problem?"

"Appearances," I say.

"Jesus Christ," she moans, blowing out a cloud of smoke and farting like a water buffalo, "fuckin' appearances."

White Rabbit

> Matter is merely mind deadened by the development
> of habit to the point where the breaking up of these
> habits is very difficult.
>
> *Rupert Sheldrake*

T HIS DREAMSTATE TALK is all well and good, but as soon
as you get out of your head and back into the world all
this stuff will seem remote and absurd. But is it? Is it just
hollow cleverness? Even if it makes sense, so what? If it's not
the world we live in, what good is any of it?

But it *is* the world we live in, if we have eyes to see. And we
do have eyes to see which we know because we already use
them. We just have to learn to use them more and better, and
it's not that hard to do.

✵

A materialist is someone who believes that physical matter is the only reality and that everything, including thoughts and emotions, can be explained in terms of physical phenomena.

Regardless of superficial beliefs, most people navigate their day-to-day lives from a materialistic perspective, which is how reality appears from the lowest and laziest point of view. This is the view from herd-level, but if we want to see more and understand better, we have to rise up above the herd. Even a small increase in elevation can make a world of difference, but how, as a practical matter, can this be achieved?

With the twin powers of focus and intent; by looking harder and seeing better.

But looking at what? Seeing what? What is it here in the seemingly materialistic universe that we can focus on so we can see through the cosmetic layer to what, if anything, lies below?

Glad you asked. Behold, the Quotidian Miracle.

Not the miracle-of-birth or sunrise or cellphone-deflects-bullet kind of miracles, but the ordinary kind that we all experience all the time, like when the phone rings and it's the person you were just thinking about. You can't prove it, you can't reproduce it, but you know it happened and you know it was more than mere coincidence because it happens too often and because you experience enough stuff like it that you know there's more to it than meets the eye. Those are quotidian, workaday miracles, and that's where you look. You look where you *know* there's more than meets the eye.

Those weird little things are what we have to become more aware of if we want to rise above herd mentality. Those are the little glimpses behind the curtain that show you where and what you really are. Most people manage to dismiss or ignore these micro-miracles and that's how they manage to maintain their pedestrian view of the world, but the mystical dimension of life is so plainly visible that you have to actively employ doublethink not to see it.

Miracles happen. The implications of that single observation can change everything, if you let it. A distracted person might see signs of a connection between his thoughts and his reality a few times a year or less. The attentive person might see these connections a few times a day or more. I myself live exclusively at this more subtle level and I know people who are much more attuned to it than me. This is the stuff we can see every day and it deserves special effort and recognition because it is the visible aspect of the unseen world where mystical is the new normal.

Commonplace miracles are your invitation to a superior understanding of being, and you accept this invitation by paying attention. We don't need big, flashy miracles to elevate ourselves above the herd, we just need to respect the little ones; the ones that don't even seem miraculous, maybe just quirky, like *deja vu* or intuition or your daily horoscope. It's like opening eyes you've never used before. That part of you that sees these tiny miracles and knows they're real is the part you want to nurture.

Perhaps you already practice some form of divination like astrology or Tarot or the *I Ching*, for instance, but don't stop there. It's not the miracle that matters, or the divination process or whatever particular clue you follow, it's *further* that matters. Following the white rabbit is the point, not who's on the phone or if it's a good day to play the ponies.

✿

If you want to pierce through the segregated cosmetic layer to the integrated structural layer of the dreamstate, you can do it the same way you do anything else. Shine the light of your mind upon it with focused intent. Begin with little miracles and progress to actively watching for pattern. See how things unfold along certain lines. Watch the relationship between your thoughts and feelings and your surroundings, between the inner and outer, between hopes and outcomes, between all the ways something didn't go and the one way it did. Feel your own energy within the larger energetic environment. Your segregation is false; the barrier between you and the Integrated State is of your own making and fueled by your own emotional energy. This integrated stuff is happening all around you all the time and you're already aware of it, so it's just a matter of seeing it more and better. Start now. Make a pronounced declaration of intent by journaling about it or writing articles or blogs or diary entries or *Dear Jed* letters or your own book; whatever helps you sharpen your powers of focus and intent. Your natural attraction got you this far, now let it take you further.

I'm kind of guessing about all this, but why not? It's there to be seen and you're able to see it, right? And the difference between non-lucid, sub-lucid and lucid is level of awareness, right? So why not? All we're really saying is that you can wake up by waking up, right? If you want to wake up, then wake up. Makes sense to me.

So that's how you do it, that's how you begin elevating

your perspective and seeing for yourself that the segregated materialistic worldview is incomplete and inaccurate, and that the integrated dreamstate is the organizational substrate where everything can be seen and understood, not as a multitude of parts, but as a unified whole. It's not the truth, but it's a much more amusing fiction.

✺

The world is transparent and all you have to do to see through it is look. Quotidian miracles are visible bits of the subtle realm, breadcrumbs you can follow, invitations that most people reject but you can accept. The real Wonderland isn't underground, it's on the surface in full illumination, but we dwell in the subterranean darkness of slumberland. These invitations are the white rabbit leading you not deeper down, but up and out.

One small step, that's all it takes to change the world. Your step to take, your world to change. Once you see it a little, it's just a matter of seeing it a little more and a little more until you see it a lot. Eventually, you can see it *in* everything *instead* of everything, like x-ray vision that allows you to see the skeletal structure of the dreamstate, as if the material world was just a cosmetic overlay concealing a far realer reality. This is the path to lucidity, to waking up *in* the dreamstate.

> Why should I wish to see God better than this day?
> I see something of God each hour of the twenty-four,
>   and each moment then;
> In the faces of men and women I see God,
>   and in my own face in the glass;
> I find letters from God dropt in the street—

and every one is sign'd by God's name,
And I leave them where they are,
    for I know that wheresoe'er I go,
Others will punctually come forever and ever.

-Walt Whitman

Whitman was on the right track, but it's not really God he's seeing, it's pattern, energy, the unity beneath the multifarious dream. This is the answer to the question you ask by reading books like this, and it's there to be seen if you know how to look. You ask yourself, *Who am I?*, and the answer is all around you all the time. The real sages have been saying it for millennia and it is true: *Tat tvam asi.* It's all you.

The Puppet Show

We are here on Earth to fart around.
Don't let anybody tell you any different.

Kurt Vonnegut

THOUGHT IS THE GREAT EQUALIZER. Anyone who can open a can of soup can think. It doesn't require money, breeding, education or great intelligence. It's like simple math; if you can add some numbers together, do a little subtraction, maybe some first-year algebra, you can think as well as anyone. Maybe not as fast, but certainly as well. You don't need education or teachers or lineage, although some writing tools and a decent library can help. You also have my books to guide you, which, at the risk of seeming immodest, offer a considerable leg up on your adventure. In any event, you start where you are and you go where you go. All serious thought eventually leads to the same place. All honest thinking is fire starting, and all fire starting ultimately leads to a scorched earth.

So yes, pretty much anyone *can* think, and pretty much everyone thinks they *do*, but pretty much no one *does*. You can see this for yourself by doing some thinking for yourself, then you'll understand what it does and why no one does it. To think honestly is to stare into the abyss, and to stare into the abyss is to enter it. Same thing. It's the scariest thing you can do, but it's the only thing that can make a difference. You can conquer nations, cure diseases, write symphonies, amass fortunes, and rise to all sorts of crazy-ass greatness, all without ever leaving your seat, or you can get up and move and discover new worlds with every step.

You're on a crowded plane heading who-knows-where, landing who-knows-when, for reasons who-knows-why. You can read the magazines and keep your seatbelt fastened and eat your plastic food and be a good little passenger, or you can return your seat to the upright position, unplug from the in-flight movie, and apply yourself to solving the mysteries that surround and define you. This entails upgrading your seat assignment from the zero-visibility aisle to the infinite-visibility window from where you can appreciate the broader dimensions of your situation which might, in turn, inspire you to take a dim view of your cramped confines which might, in turn, inspire you to kick out the emergency exit and upgrade from a fear-the-truth flightpath to a fuck-the-lie freefall. No reason not to, you now understand, since the destination is the same either way, and at least *this* way, it's *your* way. That's the difference thinking can make, but a word to the wise; if you do start thinking, stop talking. You can guess how popular fire starters and door openers are on crowded planes.

☼

We've been looking at all this stuff from the viewpoint of ego, but that makes no sense because ego is just a puppet and puppets don't have viewpoints. To really understand the dreamstate we have to see it from the perspective of singularity, so let's flip this whole thing around and see it from Brahman's side.

Beauty of the world or quintessence of dust, man delights not me; no, nor woman neither. I am not much entertained by humans or humanity or human affairs, and if the great puppet show doesn't amuse a goofball like me, how can we suppose that Brahman is amused by any of this?

The answer, the *key*, is that Brahman doesn't observe from a distance the way a moviegoer watches a film. Brahman is Atman, and Atman is *in* character *as* character. Atman doesn't just *watch* Juliet stab herself with Romeo's dagger, Atman *is* Juliet stabbing herself because, regardless of any thoughts Juliet might have on the matter, Atman *is* Juliet. Not only is Atman Juliet, there is no Juliet *but* Atman. Brahman, by way of Atman, believes itself to be you to the exact degree that you believe yourself to be you, so who's right? Probably Brahman, since he exists and you don't.

Atman is Brahman rendered not only finite, but egobound and dreambound as well. Atman is not a detached observer, but the very selfhood of the character in which it resides. When you say I-Am/Consciousness, it's Atman speaking. You aren't deluded into forgetting you are Atman, rather, Atman is deluded into forgetting it is Brahman. But first, Brahman is self-deluded into believing it is Atman; that's the original sin, so to speak, the Prime Deception. Your ego is not actually *your* ego because there is no actual *you*. Viewed aright, it is Atman that is egoically benighted, not you. You're not the deceived, you're the deception. You're a puppet wanting to achieve oneness with the hand up its butt, but dude, that's not your hand. You're Pinocchio wishing the Blue Fairy will make you real, but you're just a block of wood and the underlying truth of you is no-you. The real magic of the dreamstate doesn't come from Maya deceiving *you* but from Brahman deceiving *itself.* From our perspective, Atman is Brahman, but from Brahman's perspective, Atman is a dolled-up hand putting on a show, and the trick for Brahman is forgetting it's his own hand he's looking at. If Brahman can do that, then awareness can be amused by appearance and we have a working dreamstate.

Seriously, you didn't learn all this in grade school?

In a better creation myth, it's not Adam and Eve who are transformed by the apple, but God/Brahman who eats the Fruit of the Tree of the False-Knowledge of Duality and sinks into the dream of segregated awareness. In truth, there is no you or me or Atman or Maya, there is *only* Brahman. Brahman is dreamer, dreaming and dreamt; perceiver, perception and perceived. In the dreamstate, Brahman is artificially partitioned into Atman so it gets to dream the dream of self, but it's not *my* self because there is no me, and it's not *Atman's* self because there is no Atman. It's *Brahman's* self because there is only consciousness.

✿

I am, by my own lights, the coolest, most awesome person ever, and I hope that you, by your own lights, are the coolest, most awesome person ever too. It's nice. If I could have dinner with anyone in all of history, I would have dinner with me, and I do it all the time through internal and externalized thought. Thinking for me is like puzzle-solving, and what better puzzle than reality? What is this magic box we find ourselves in but a puzzle box? At first, I attacked the puzzle with a manic compulsion, but since solving it, I have continued to play with it and admire it and share what I've learned.

Why shouldn't you be the coolest, most awesome person ever by your own lights? You are the universe, the totality. This is a hard fact whether there are zillions of us, or just you. This is not just a pretty snowflake story that says you're special because we're all special, this is the literal truth that says if you are self-aware, then you are Atman which is Brahman which is all.

I'll say that again: If you are self-aware, then you are Atman which is Brahman which is all. That's not some quasi-mystical New Age bullshit, that's the irreducible bottom line of being. You might prefer the pretty snowflake story, but this story is true. For what it's worth, you are The One, and that's not nothing.

Wisefool Press

Books by Jed McKenna

THE ENLIGHTENMENT TRILOGY

SPIRITUAL ENLIGHTENMENT
THE DAMNEDEST THING

SPIRITUALLY INCORRECT ENLIGHTENMENT

SPIRITUAL WARFARE

THE DREAMSTATE TRILOGY

JED MCKENNA'S THEORY OF EVERYTHING
THE ENLIGHTENED PERSPECTIVE

PLAY: A PLAY BY JED MCKENNA

DREAMSTATE: A CONSPIRACY THEORY

WWW.WISEFOOLPRESS.COM

Bonus Content

A Game with No Name

Fool and Wise Man, hand-in-hand,
Set out to settle a flap.
"There's trouble ahead," the Wise Man said,
"So don your thinking cap!"
At this the Fool turned red and said;
"I think I smell a trap!"

"I fear for you," the Wise Man said,
"Your brain is much too small.
Perhaps you ought to stretch it out,
Like cities when they sprawl.
Until it can be seen from space,
Just like the Chinese Wall!"

"My brain is fine," the Fool decried,
"It's *yours* that's much too big.
You seek to do experiments,
With me your guinea pig!
So a game we'll play, the loser to pay,
By dancing the winner a jig!"

The Wise Man and the Fool were friends,
Or so the story goes.
The former of the latter asked,
"What game do you propose?"
To which the latter quick replied,
"The game that no one knows!"

The life of a Fool is a curious one,
Of a Wise Man doubly so.
There's ups and downs and all arounds,
And kerfuffling hither and fro,
But something there's not, at least, not a lot,
Is abundance of sorrow and woe.

"It is said," said the Fool, "as a general rule,
That in life we all wear many faces."
"Not me! Not I!" said his friend with a sigh.
"Though I hasten to add,
That when still but a lad,
I wore six faces that this one replaces."

"If no one knows this game of yours,"
The Wise Man asked politely,
"Then how do we dare, a winner declare,
In a manner most forthrightly?
For if perchance 'tis I must dance,
Rules mustn't be treated lightly!"

"The rules, you see, are only three,"
The Fool said lickety-split.
"The second and third are somewhat blurred,
But the first is in marble writ.
So behold my surprise to realize,
I cannot think of it!"

The Fool said, "It starts, in thirty-three parts,
 But my sense of the middle is muddled."
"Then let's start at the end, my curious friend,"
 Said the Wise Man, and thusly they huddled.
 But rather than finding the answers they sought,
 They both just grew more befuddled.

 So with a fiddledy-dum and twiddledy-dee,
 They searched high and low for rules to see.
"Not here! Not there!" cried the Wise Man,
 Said the Fool, "I see only thee!"
 They were as if blind, so no rules could they find,
 From the roof of the sky to the floor of the sea.

"I'm hopelessly puzzled and swizzled and fuzzled,"
 Quoth the Wise Man in solemnest tones.
"My madness is such that my sadness is much,
 And I'm feeling an ache in my bones.
 So answer me this; Would I be quite remiss,
 If I questioned your game of unknowns?"

"The rules are the same for the game with no name,
 As this game of pretending we're playing.
 So well might you wonder, if the Fool made a blunder,
 Which I doubt you'd find very dismaying.
 But don't get too queasy, the game should be easy,
 At least," said the Fool, "that's what I'm praying."

So the Wise Man replied, "You're a marvelous guide,
And I'm enjoying our game very highly,
But perhaps it could be, that you're less fool than me,
And you're playing the game very slyly."
To which, said the Fool, fearing dire misrule,
"I suspect that it's *you* who is wily."

So Wise Man and Fool invented new rules,
That a fool can be wise and the wise can be fools.
And they both seemed to see, and both did agree,
What they don't teach in books or in schools;
In a game without stakes there are no lucky breaks,
No one wins in a game without rules.

The Wise Man saluted, 'twas well executed,
And the Fool bowed low to the ground.
Though admitting defeat was quite bittersweet,
They each saw the other one crowned.
Now it happened to chance that they *both* owed a dance,
And they started to leap and to bound.

So they danced and whirled, and pranced and twirled,
And they hipped and hopped, and tripped and flopped.
They cavorted and capered and frolic'd and spun,
'Til the rise of the moon saw the set of the sun.
And they both saw quite clearly what was hidden to some,
That you can't lose a game that's not meant to be won.

-JM

Twelve Ways to Say One Thing

The miracle, or the power, that elevates the few, is to be
found in their industry, application, and perseverance
under the promptings of a brave, determined spirit.

Mark Twain

"I WISH YOU WROTE MORE ABOUT prayer and affirmations
and all that stuff," says Maggie, apropos of nothing. It
takes me a minute to understand what she means.

"There's not a lot to say about it," I reply. I'm in my comfy
chair in front of a low fire, she's somewhat behind me on the
couch.

"There are plenty of books about it," she says. "Movies too.
A lot of people are really interested in this stuff."

"Okay," I say, "and what has this to do with me?"

"Just that you should say more about it," she says.

"Like, in a book?" I ask.

"In the book you're working on, *Dreamstate*, right? Isn't manifestation a dreamstate thing? Wouldn't there be a lot you could say about it?"

Fair enough.

"There's a lot to say about it if you don't know what it is," I say, "but the main thing is to make the transition from human-born to self-born and find out for yourself. Worry about achieving lucidity and the manifestation stuff takes care of itself. The books you're talking about are for people who don't understand that, so they're trying to dance without learning to stand. Naturally, the effect is slightly grotesque."

Maggie's making an effort to form a connection, and I'm making an effort not to, which, I realize, is not what I want to do.

"I had a roommate who was into *A Course In Miracles*. Have you read that?"

I deny voice to an internal groan, but with a twinge of nostalgia because I don't get to groan about this stuff much anymore. As I recall, I would have been sternly intolerant of this sort of empty talk back when I felt some responsibility to guide people away from flowery trappings, but Maggie's not a student and I'm not a teacher. I'm just an honorary uncle and she has asked a question about something I know something about. If she really cared, I'd offer to make arrangements so she could spend a few months with Sonaya, who lives and breathes at the level of pattern and manifestation, but Maggie isn't that interested. She's somewhere between politely interested and personally interested, which is not very interested at all.

"I spent some time with the *Course* and peripheral works

a long time ago," I say. "It had a nice authoritative tone, as I recall, but I prefer the authority that comes from being right rather than sounding right. In any event, the critical distinction is always the same; miracles and manifestation are natural properties of adulthood. Adulthood is what matters, the ability to shape and influence reality is just part of the deal. Prior to the advent of lucidity, the only worthwhile use of manifestation would be to bring about the advent of lucidity."

☼

She's been looking at more than just *ACIM*, she informs me. She also mentions a recent crop of books and docutainment-type films that promote this sort of thing to the muddled masses; typical spiritual marketplace fare where merit is based on popularity which is based on sugar content. What's not popular about the idea that we're all little Harrys and Hermiones and life is just a great big Hogwarts? They even trot out some modern high priests, physicists, to support their correct but entry-level discovery that there's more to life than meets the eye. In other words, what should rightfully be a grade school subject of brief duration has been elevated to a semi-mystical pseudo-science with enough glitter to enchant the largest and least sophisticated audience.

Obviously, I should read the books and watch the movies if I'm going to be critical of them, but it's not really necessary and I don't really want to. If the books and movies Maggie's referring to actually brought about change or improvement, if anyone responded to them by altering course from downward entrenchment to forward progress, I'd take a particular interest, but they only amount to a minor fad that had its fifteen minutes and disappeared. The topic itself is enduring, and *ACIM* is probably best-in-field, so I'm grateful that she's interested in that instead of some infomercial-quality 3-disc set on the wonders of wishcraft.

I'm guessing that Maggie wants to spend time with me but has discovered that I'm not very easy to talk to. It's not that I'm unfriendly in particular, just that I can't hold up my end of a normal conversation. We spent some time discussing films, but our tastes and interest levels don't match up; I'm currently fixated on Béla Tarr, and she's into low-budget indies. In music, I have a thing for Arvo Pärt at the moment, and when she tells me what she's into, I don't even know what she said. I'm currently amused by economics and world affairs because I enjoy storms and I see dark clouds rolling in, but that's just for my personal viewing pleasure and there's nothing to discuss. We tried talking about some other stuff, but the disconnect was just too wide. She's repeating our past by trying to squeeze herself into my tiny sphere of interest. I appreciate her effort and I want to do my part if I can. I remind myself that she's not visiting me in the cabin because I'm so witty and delightful, but because she's a young person on top of a lonely mountain and I represent a minor novelty. I'm sure that if we lived in Manhattan I'd never see her.

"But it's possible, right?" she asks. "You don't have to be a human adult like you mean? Anyone can do miracle stuff?"

"To some degree, naturally," I say. "Everyone can and does do, uh, miracle stuff all the time, and maybe a segregated person could do it better than an integrated person if they followed the instructions in books, I don't really know. It might be more a function of alignment than degree of wake-fulness. I suppose whoever tries harder will do better. Careful what you wish for is always good advice."

1-3 - ORDER OF DIFFICULTY

"I made a copy of the list of fifty principles of miracles from the beginning of the *Course*," she says. "I thought it would be fun to ask you about it."

I can think of two or three reasons she'd want to do this for herself. The only reason I'd want to do it, besides having a moderately interesting topic to discuss with Maggie, is that it might be something for the book.

"Sure, we can try, if you take notes. Yes?"

"Yes."

"Okay, what's the first one? No degree of difficulty?"

She pulls some sheets of paper out of her back pocket and unfolds them.

"No order of difficulty," she says, "right."

"That's correct."

She gets up and grabs pen and paper and sinks back into a corner of the couch in such a way that she's facing me and I can see her if I turn my head. Maya volunteers to act as her foot warmer. I watch the fire and wonder if I want to cover this stuff in the book and if *ACIM*'s fifty principles list is the way to do it. Maybe, to both. Sometimes I get book material written out and polished to near-readiness before I decide against using it, and sometimes I'm surprised how good things are for which I had little hope, so I am very open to ignoring any initial reluctance I may feel, especially if someone else is volunteering to participate. My time is not so valuable that I can't indulge in little forays into realms of fancy, and I am not so swamped by viable offers of companionship that I can be dismissive of someone as pleasant and eager as Maggie.

"Okay," I say, "before we start, let's just establish something. Anything I have to say about this is based on my personal understanding, that's all. I'm no expert. There's not much actual knowledge involved, just reason and experience, and I'm sure there are factors and influences about which I know nothing. There are subjects on which I can speak with perfect authority, and this isn't one of them."

"Done with your little disclaimer?" she asks.

"I reserve the right to…"

"Noted. So you agree there's no order of difficulty."

"Yes. There's no issue of scale. Size and difficulty don't matter, except maybe insofar as they cloud the mind with doubt. If the elements are in place and the obstacles aren't, it works. Also, there's no judgment, in case that doesn't come up later. There's no question of worthiness."

"So it's like magic?"

"It's like CGI. There's no difference between creating a molecule, a tree, a forest, a planet, or a galaxy. It's all the same level of difficulty."

"The next one, two, says miracles don't matter."

"Miracle is a poor word choice."

"What's the right word? Manifestation?"

"No, that still reflects a child's-eye view. Flow, integration, alignment, co-creation, that sort of thing. It's a natural by-product of being in tune. Get yourself in order and this stuff just sorts itself out."

"Maybe you should invent a word," she suggests.

"It's not the word that eludes me, it's the idea. It's not something you can isolate without losing it, like trying to capture sunlight in your hands. The Integrated State, as the name is meant to imply, is not made of parts. A miracle is not a subroutine of some larger program, as it might appear from the segregated perspective, or as it's packaged by vendors. You're a dream character in a dream universe, but the two, self and environment, are really one."

"That sounds very mystical."

"I suppose."

"Can we stick with the word miracle, just to make it easy?"

"Under mild protest," I grumble. "I might prefer co-creation."

"Noted. So, do miracles matter?"

"No," I say, "not in and of themselves. They're just the way things work."

"What about Jesus walking on water or turning water into wine and all that?"

"Yes, or Jack's magic beans or Samantha's twitchy nose."

She scribbles her notes.

"Not admitting the Bible into evidence, I guess."

"I guess not."

"Let's see," she says, "number three. Miracles come from love. Love is the source…"

"No, sorry, we can't bend it that far. We'd have to totally redefine love to make it fit. Not necessary or interesting, too much effort, very misleading. The *Course* is reshaping this subject to fit within its own framework, but this subject stands fine on its own. Next."

"So it's wrong?" she asks.

"What do you mean?"

"You're saying the *Course* is wrong?"

"Not so much wrong as distorted. Why, what did you think?"

"Well, I mean, I just thought, it seems so… I don't know."

"It's written from and for the segregated perspective. The *Course* isn't like wisdom or truth, it's just a modern Christian remix, but you can't remix nonsense into sense. If the figures don't add up, you don't try to massage them, you erase the board and start over."

"But what about prayer and all that?"

"I can certainly see where religious systems would want to lay claim to the co-creative process, treat it as God's power or grace, make it proprietary and use it to support their beliefs, but the religious element takes us in the wrong direction and only serves to reinforce an immature understanding. You don't need to dress co-creation up in a religious motif; that suggests that there's judgment or a worthiness factor, which there's not. The wicked manifest desires as well as the just, maybe better since the hotter emotions are more powerful."

"Really? That doesn't sound right."

"Right or just?"

"I don't know, both, I guess."

"Close your eyes."

"Okay."

"Picture some happy, mellow people."

"Okay."

"What are they doing?"

"Nothing," she says. "Sitting around."

"Do you want to make a movie about them?"

"Can't," she says, "there's nothing going on."

"Exactly. They're content. They're not driven to change or fix or create anything. Without discontent, there's no drama or conflict. The director yells action and nothing happens. If you want to make them interesting, you have to firebomb their happiness, get them up and moving, like God did to Ken and Barbie. Then, unfocused emotional energy can be focused on something and the story can begin. It might be nice to be happy, but it's not entertaining. Creators and destroyers are half-mad or more, and it's that madness that powers change and manifests reality. I know, I've been completely mad."

There's a pause as she writes.

"I don't think it says anything like that in the *Course*," she says.

"It wouldn't. "It's a book for people with wishy-washy emotions that beget wishy-washy results. Prayer is a process of emotionally fueled desire and when it doesn't work, there's a problem with either the process or the perception of it."

I pause and reflect on Maggie's perspective.

"I guess you thought you were wielding a document of greater spiritual heft," I say.

"I don't know," she says. "I thought it would be simpler."

"It *is* simpler, that's the point. It gets junked up with a lot of wrong-knowing, but once you get out of the mud it's as simple as sunlight. We don't have to go on if you don't want."

"I do want to."

"Me too. Just because it's not super accurate doesn't mean

it's not valuable. Anything of value will need to be sugar-coated to survive and thrive in the spiritual marketplace, so all we're doing is peeling back the outer layers to see what's underneath and, relatively speaking, it's pretty good. I can't think of anything better you might have come up with."

"Oh," she says brightly, "yay."

4, 5 - The Spiritual Sense

"Four, miracles mean life. God is the giver of…"

"Next."

"Hold on," she says, "this one says God's voice will direct you, you'll be told all you need to know."

"Well, okay, I see what it means. Cloaking such a simple process in fairytale trappings only muddies the waters, but the general idea is right. When you awaken in the dreamstate, you learn new ways of knowing and understanding and navigating. To call it God's voice reinforces a segregated perspective, whereas the thing you're tapping into is your own broader dimension. The universe is mind and you are mind, so any distinction between the two is necessarily artificial."

"God's voice isn't really a voice?"

"No, it's a sense, the spiritual sense; right-knowing, right-action, that stuff."

"Intuition?"

"Sure, the inner voice. When everything is in alignment, then there's no energetic static and this inner voice can be tuned in clearly. Once the spiritual sense is awakened, old ways are forgotten and people who operate by those old ways appear functionally handicapped."

"Like me?"

"Yes and no. You're a good example of someone who is centered and focused. On the scale of sub-lucidity, I'd put you pretty high toward near-lucid, probably as a factor of your own self-development and your mother's influence. You're doing exactly what you should be doing. You're playing in the playground; going to school, living in the city, having relationships, learning to make movies. You have a clear sense of identity and direction. I know I make this stuff sound like awake is right and asleep is wrong, but it's not like that. I'd love to be in your shoes. Don't get hung up on judgment, just do what you want and make stuff happen. As the Thelemites say, 'Do what thou wilt shall be the whole of the law.'"

"What's a Thelemite?"

"Hell if I know, but that's what they say."

"But I'd be better off if I was in the Integrated State, right? Then I could…?"

"Someday, maybe, no rush. It comes with a price. Play, create, have fun. The combination of focus and intent is all you need. Bring those two things to bear on any endeavor and you'll have more magic on your side than you can shake a wand at. Doors will appear in solid walls, the universe will reshape itself to your desire. This is true. Whatever you want, the recipe is always the same. Focus and intent. Focus being the mental aspect and intent the emotional."

"And alignment?"

"Alignment is a learned sense. We can compare it to balance which is really achieved through a process of microcorrections at an imperceptible level, so what looks like positive balance is really negative *im*balance. Alignment works the same way. You course-correct based on subtle stirrings of not-rightness."

"So alignment is the important thing?"

"Yes, if you're not egoically misaligned, not swimming against the current, then you can expect your authentic desires to naturally unfold. It's like the tires on your car. If they're even slightly out of balance or misaligned, a vibration will be amplified through the car and into your body and you will register it as not-rightness. Some people drive around in old rattletraps and have a very high tolerance for a rough ride, others are more refined and are very sensitive to even the slightest tremor. If you wanted to enjoy clear access to your internal resources, it's easy to see that a quiet vehicle would facilitate that and a loud one would drown it out."

"Okay," she says, writing, "what internal resources?"

"Well, the vibration could be understood as emotion and the inner resources as thought, but even those terms are really metaphors. Imagine trying to do some math in your head while your annoying friend yells out random numbers."

"You make emotion the bad guy a lot."

"Only inasmuch as it conflicts with clarity of mind. The ocean in which we swim is mind, not heart. Maybe *we* are the heart, maybe we're the heart in a sea of mind. I guess we can't rule that out since it's effectively the case."

"Like the universe is all mind, but it was missing heart so God created us," she says. "That's nice, I like that."

She writes it out and circles it so I won't forget she likes it.

"Anyway," I continue, "yes, alignment is much more important than miracles. A miracle is like a cool power that a child would naturally want to possess, but it's just the visible aspect of something much bigger and better. More interesting than performing miracles would be following them back to see where they come from. That's where it gets interesting."

She writes, reads what she wrote, and asks her next question.

"And you don't have to be in the integrated state for miracles to work, right? This stuff works for everyone?"

"Yes," I say, "but again, what's the point of improving your incarceration when you can just end it?"

I ask rhetorically, but forget to tell her that.

"Happiness?" she suggests. "A nicer life? Maybe it makes sense to stay in what you call the sub-lucid state and have these nice abilities like intuition and deeper knowing and co-creation and stuff."

I make a grumpy sound.

"Yes," I say reluctantly, "I agree. I'm not used to addressing that particular point of view, but it's certainly valid. Compared to my assumed audience, the reader as I imagine him or her, you're like a civilian, a noncombatant. I usually work on the assumption that I'm speaking to people who specifically want to move forward, but if you just want to have a better experience of the dreamstate, as you're saying, I'd say sure, why not? The universe is your instrument, play it however you want."

"But that's not your normal advice?"

"Normally I don't see any reason for people to be happy in a dungeon when they can just leave. Their chains aren't locked, the door's not bolted, so why stay? Getting out of the dungeon should be the goal, not making the best of it."

"But that's not what I should be doing?"

"Not really, not now, not until it seems like a dungeon instead of a carnival. When it's time to go you won't have to ask. You're in a great place, don't go out of your way to make it wrong. Next one?"

"Five. Miracles should be involuntary. I guess that means they should happen naturally."

"Yes, it becomes a natural thing, not something you have to perform according to rules like a magic formula from a book of spells or something. You don't need procedures, you just need to have some clarity and allow things to unfold."

"It says conscious miracles can be misguided."

"If we take conscious to mean egoic as opposed to authentic, then sure, they'd necessarily be misguided. And let me just reiterate; this whole thing, reality, the universe, is all mind and nothing else. The dreamstate is mind and you are mind. Emotion forms the barrier that allows us to dwell in an artificially segregated condition, but segregation is an artificial sub-state of the larger artificial state we call reality. That doesn't make it bad or negative or evil, just walled off from universal mind. Incidentally, that's the wall Ahab says the prisoner should thrust through, the wall represented by the white whale. When the wall is dismantled and you're reunited with universal mind, then you operate at the level of emotionally powered thought, which we're calling focus and intent, okay?"

"That's really good," she says, writing quietly for the next minute.

"How can miracles be misguided?" she asks.

"By being egoic rather than authentic, meaning the process is misunderstood or fear-based or just somehow out of alignment. The term misguided is a bit misguided. In and out of alignment are betters ways to think of it."

"Okay," she says, "next one…"

"How many more of these?" I ask.

"Forty-five."

"No way. Let me see."

She hands me the pages. I scan the list, relieved to see that we'll be skipping over large chunks. I return the pages and she sinks back into her seat.

"And why are we doing this?" I ask.

"I don't know. For me, for you, for the book you're working on? Maybe just for something to talk about. You're not the easiest person to talk to, you know."

"Take good notes."

"I know the drill."

"And try to skip over the God and love stuff."

"Even though it might be the right idea by the wrong name?"

"You are your mother's daughter," I say. "Next."

6, 7 - SURRENDER & RELEASE

"Six," she says, "miracles are natural…"

"Yes."

"When they don't occur…" She continues.

"Something's wrong," I interrupt. "You're out of balance which would probably have an emotional cause. It happens. You wait, breathe, get centered until everything is back on track. Next?"

"Seven. Miracles are everyone's right, but you have to go

through purification."

"The word right is wrong, but the idea is right. Purification would mean the casting off of ego and rebirth into the eyes-open state. Purification is too much word; surrender and release are better. You release the illusion of control, which is ego, and relax into the energetic environment, which is the dreamstate."

"And then you know what your path is?"

"Path? That's not on the list."

"I'm asking."

"By path, you mean direction or life-purpose or something?"

"Yeah, like what you're supposed to do in life, like you and the books."

"Okay, then I'd say yes. Once you allow ego to settle out of the way, then you would naturally find your authentic direction of travel, and you'd have this co-creative thing going so everything would be naturally enhanced."

She pauses in her writing.

"Enhanced?"

"Smooth, effortless, frictionless. A kind of inner genius emerges; the spiritual sense again. You naturally begin functioning at the level of pattern and everything works differently. You gradually learn to discard the old ways and allow the new, and that's how you grow into this enhanced mode of being."

"But purification or surrender is not necessary?"

"No, anyone can manifest desires and see this stuff at work for themselves. It's going on all the time in the normal course of simply being. That's why there's so much interest in prayer and manifestation and affirmations and all that, because everyone has a direct experience of it. People see it in their own lives so they know it works and want to do it better."

"So it works?"

"Seems to."

"What if you don't like your path?"

"Then it's not your path."

I wonder about her interest level.

"Are you enjoying all this?" I ask. "Conversationally or otherwise?"

She thinks for a moment.

"Yes," she says, "so far. I can see that if someone wants to talk to you they have to kind of come to you like this. I wouldn't be able to drag you over into my interests."

"But why would you want to talk to me at all? Never mind, I withdraw the question. I'm glad you're here. This is very pleasant. Go ahead. Tell me when you're tired."

"I'm a college kid, I can go for days. You tell me when *you're* tired, old man."

✲

Here's what I don't tell Maggie because she'd have a lot of questions and I wouldn't want to say more than I'll say here.

I have personal experience of co-creation that is so far beyond anything I've ever heard or read about that I'm almost in disbelief myself. In conjunction with others—mainly Sonaya, who we might remember from the first book—I have been closely involved with acts of dreamstate co-creation of such immensity, complexity, and specificity that they make the usual getting-what-you-want stuff seem like ordering a pizza by comparison. Even to say a little more would be to say too much, but I will say that if there is any limit to what can be accomplished through the co-creative process, I have no idea what it might be.

I should add these particular situations did not rely on any manner of specialized knowledge or sophisticated techniques. Yes, the participants were uncommonly well established in the Integrated State, but the processes involved were no different for things of great magnitude than small. And, as is always the case, outcomes and timing far exceeded hopes.

It is my opinion, based on experience, that planetary courses could be altered and stars extinguished in basically the same way you'd get a good parking space or find the right puppy. The same rules apply. If the elements are in place—if the desire is authentic and the emotion is focused—then the process infallibly works. Co-creation is a natural phenomenon that obeys natural laws, and if you are a self-aware being in the self-aware universe, you are capable of things you wouldn't believe.

✿

Maggie continues, unaware of my lengthy digression.

"One guy says the key to happiness is to accept the inevitable," she informs me.

"One guy?"

"A spiritual teacher guy. Isn't acceptance of the inevitable the same as surrender?"

A spiritual teacher guy says the key to happiness is to accept the inevitable? Oh my, where to begin...

"That might work to a degree, but non-resistance is a half-measure, and if it's still ego doing the non-resisting, then it's just an ego-preserving tactic; a cheat that only cheats the cheater. Passivity isn't the point."

"It worked for Gandhi," she quips.

"Well, not to badmouth the Mahatma, but what works against a civilized nation behaving badly on the world stage is hardly a universal solution. Try passive resistance with Stalin or Mao and see where it gets you."

"I never thought about that."

"The real thing is a balance between dynamically interwoven energies. The only thing that matters…"

"…is actually becoming an adult," she finishes. "Yeah, okay. Ready?"

"Yep."

"It's not your nap time yet?"

"Don't make fun of naps, young person."

8, 9 - HEALING & ALIGNMENT

"This is the eighth one. Are miracles healing? Do they supply a lack? Are they done for those with more for those with less?"

I parse her words for anything that resonates. Some of it does a little, but we have to maintain a reasonable coherence threshold or she really will keep me from my siesta.

"There's nothing there to work with."

"Nothing?"

"More effort than it's worth."

"Okay, nine, are miracles a kind of exchange?"

"Between what parties?"

"Uh," she reads in bits, "love, reverse physical laws, giver and receiver."

"It's not a clear thought and I don't want to try to fix it. Next one."

"I'm surprised you're putting up with this. You didn't like this subject in your books."

"I thought I covered it more than adequately, but there's no reason not say more about how the creative process works; maybe accidentally write a bestseller."

"Ooh, that'd be cool."

"Yeah, cool," I agree. "I could go on the *Good Morning Show* and tell Bob and Cindy fun ways to ask for a raise or find their soulmate, maybe whip up my secret recipe for noodles macaroni."

"You're not a big TV watcher, I take it."

"Sit on a stool with *Millionaire* guy and Patty Lee and discuss reality and provide tips for looking ten years younger."

"You did it for my mom. Twenty years. Seriously. People think she's my sister."

"She did it for herself, and it's not a miracle, it's the correction of an error, the removal of an artificial obstruction. A blockage was cleared and rightness was restored. That's all we're really talking about, correction of a problem, the source of the problem being ego which, by the way, is not an archvillain but an essential dreamstate facilitator. If there were somewhere better to be and ego was keeping us from it, that would be bad, but there's not. I'm rambling. Where are we?"

"So *she* did it? My mother made herself younger and healthier and happier and everything?"

"The lines can be a little blurred, but yes, her rejuvenation was her, not me. I've seen it many times."

"So you're not her guardian angel?"

I have to think about that for a moment.

"I've been tempted to use that term when the exact right person came along at the exact right time," I reply. "Someone who might seem very unlikely in all respects, but they fit the specific needs of a specific situation like a key in a lock, and then they're gone. Understood this way, anyone can be anyone's guardian angel at some time. A skid row bum got me out of a tight spot near the Port Authority once when I was a kid. His appearance and assistance were tremendously unlikely. When I think of guardian angels, he comes to mind. There are no voids or gaps in pattern, but sometimes a patch in the fabric stands out a bit."

"Okay," she says, "but what happened to mom was like a healing. That was the eighth one. Are miracles healing?"

"Going from misalignment to alignment is healing," I say. "We can be egoically misshapen, but when the deforming influence is released we have the elasticity to regain our proper shape. That's what your mother did, she corrected a misalign-ment, like spiritual chiropractic, maybe. Misalignment is debilitating, so being restored to rightness looks like healing. My appearance in your mother's life at the right time was her miracle, not mine, but, by the same token, the appearance of you and your mother and grandfather was perfect for the book I was working on, and I serve the books, so I guess it was balanced or bilateral or something, in case that's on your list."

"So it was an exchange?"

"There was balance."

She spends a few minutes writing the notes which I'll later write out to see how I feel about it. I use the time to wonder why I don't keep the wine closer to where I drink it. It sounds like a good idea, I reflect, but it's probably not.

"This is like a historical record," Maggie says as she writes. "Like I'm serving a purpose by getting you to answer all these questions while we still have you."

"Still have me? Jesus, it's not a deathbed interview."

"When I'm your age, you'll be dead, and I'll be like, shit, I was with that guy. I should have picked his brain."

"So that's what we're doing? Harvesting my mind fruit?"

"I mean, here's just this one book, right? *ACIM*, real popular, millions of copies sold, but it's really not very good, is it?"

"You're asking?"

"Yes."

"I recall thinking it was quite an impressive document back when I looked into it. I wouldn't say it's bad, but it's written from a childish perspective for children who want to play grown-up without growing up. Why cater to that demographic?"

"Okay, why?"

"Why what?"

"Why cater to that demographic?"

"Oh, yeah, right. Good question. The reason for catering to a childish readership is because sub-lucidity is the official status of the dreamstate, the optimal dreamstate condition. We exist in a Goldilocks range of lucidity; not too smart, not too dumb."

"See?" she says. "How many people do you think know this stuff? How many people could sit here like this and take a subject like this and make it clear?"

"So I'm your project now? Is this for your script?"

"Maybe. I don't know. Do you always know why you do things?"

10 - THE MISUSE OF MIRACLES

"The next one is number ten, it's about miracles as spectacles."

"That would be a misunderstanding."

"Yeah, a misunderstanding, that's what it says."

"Doing something to show off or prove something is inconceivable to me. My minds recoils from the idea. I'm sure I couldn't even do it. I can point to my own experiences and use them to illustrate how things work, but the idea that I could do tricks or something... I don't see anything like that. There's a real delicateness to this stuff, you can't just go horsing around with it. *I* couldn't, anyway. If someone had an authentic desire, if they were so configured, if they were aligned in such a way, maybe, but really, I don't know. I hesitate to say anything is impossible in the dreamstate, but misuse of miracles might be. It makes no sense."

"Okay," she says. "Is it like surrender to a higher power?"

"I don't think of it that way. It's more like you stop swimming against the current, stop fighting the ocean, that's all. If you were a fish, would you think of the ocean as a higher power? Or just the energetic environment in which you swim and play? You might not even have a clear idea of where you end and the ocean begins. To me, it's more like directed energy. You relax into it and allow yourself to swim with the current, and when you do that, you discover that where things are going and where you want to go are exactly the same. This is where you recognize the distinction between egoic and authentic desire."

"Isn't that what I said before? Accept the inevitable?"

"Okay, two points. One, what you said seemed lacking in the interactive component, more like abdication than co-creative participation. What I'm describing is like swimming with the current, and what you said sounded like going limp and being carried along. I'm a little sensitive to that distinction because it seems like an easy trap to fall into. Two, it wasn't really something you said, it was something you repeated. If it were really coming from you, it would have had more weight behind it."

She makes notes and I wonder if I'm speaking indelicately, which I can do without meaning to. When she speaks again I realize that she's totally immune to my lack of charm.

"So," she repeats, "no showing off?"

"The issue of spectacle doesn't really have an integrated counterpart. That's what I mean when I say it's inconceivable to me. I suppose an ego-based person might think that way and that's who the *Course* is for. There's no need for spectacle."

"To induce belief, it says."

"I know it does, but induce belief why? I don't remember if the author is supposed to be Jesus, but wasn't it Jesus who performed miracles to induce belief? Never mind, I don't want to go there. An ego-based person might want to do tricks to impress others, but no one who is awake in the dreamstate would think like that, so we can say this addresses a juvenile level of understanding."

"Which makes sense."

"Sure. We're not trying to judge the list, we're just trying to extract the meaning."

"So it's right that the use of miracles for spectacle is a misunderstanding?"

"It's a juvenile understanding. It always comes back to that. Next one, if you're not too bored."

11, 12 - THE MEDIUM OF MIRACLES

"Eleven. I'm cutting this one way back. Is prayer the medium of miracles?"

"Medium meaning user interface, I guess. At the beginner level it is, but it's like training wheels on a bike. You learn to balance and you don't need them anymore. Focused emotional energy is the real co-creative interface; the thing between a clear vision and its full realization. The process is organic, it doesn't need to be converted into words. It doesn't even require conscious volition. When you're learning to dance you might have to count in your head and focus on your feet, but as you get better, that extra layer of mental participation is discarded. You might start out using a technique like prayer or affirmations, but then, as you get the hang of it, the verbalizing becomes superfluous. I think that sounds right."

"So you don't pray? You don't verbalize?"

"I'm not a good example. That would just confuse the issue."

"Because?"

"For you or the book?"

"I don't know. Stop asking."

"Okay, let's see. In me, there is no desire. I don't want anything, and except for a normal aversion to pain and boredom, I don't really care what happens. For anyone established in the Integrated State, the process has gone from coarse, like the use of conscious desire and prayer, to subtle, so that nothing like a sharp desire ever arises; no jagged spikes, just a nice smooth waveform. I don't know if it's helpful to hear about that."

"It seems interesting if that's where all this goes; if that's the ultimate, you know, goal or state or whatever."

"You're writing down your parts too, I hope."

"Yes," she says.

"Okay, I guess there's no reason not to talk about it. So, in my particular case, there's no ego, no desire. What the universe wants and what I want are therefore in perfect harmony and no input from me is needed. I swim but I don't steer. I can see how the power of prayer or affirmation might sound pretty good to people, but to me, that would be like living in a paint shaker. My experience is one of effortless flow. I enjoy the process as it unfolds. I admire it, but I don't take an active hand. My life is an allowing; the direction I go is the one that mysteriously opens before me."

"Can I just say…?"

"Go ahead."

"Your life isn't exactly what people dream about. You live alone in an old cabin, no family, you don't seem to own anything, you don't do much. I'm not trying to offend you, but…"

"Don't worry about offending me. I understand what you're saying and, like I said, I'm not a good example. There's a paradigm thing we're crossing when we start talking about me that only confuses the issue. My life is very dialed-in. Yes, I have everything I want, but the other side of that is that I don't want much. I should add that, by normal standards, I am a very powerful wizard; I can't imagine wanting something and not being able to get it."

"Then why don't you have a microwave?" she asks.

"A microwave?"

"I don't know, some good speakers? A nice car? Wifi?"

"I'm simple, not poor. If I want something I get it. If I want to go somewhere, I go. If I want to do something, I do it. I'm not a shut-in."

"I think maybe you are."

"I prefer recluse," I say, "maybe hermit. Okay, one more."

"I think we covered this. Twelve, are miracles thoughts?"

"Certainly, in the sense that the dreamstate is a thought. That's the key to the whole thing. Thought is the medium of the dreamstate—medium like environment, not interface—if that doesn't conflict too much with my last answer."

"We'll fix it in post."

"Whatever the dreamstate is, and whatever thought is, they are, correctly understood, the same thing. In the same way that the dreamstate is intelligence and your interface with it is emotionally powered intelligence, something like that. Did we finish that question?"

"It says there's a body level of thought and spiritual level of thought and they create the physical and spiritual worlds."

"There are no different worlds because there are no worlds,

there's only the dreamstate. Wherever you are, there you are. There's nowhere else to be but here. You can experience it differently through modification at the level of perception—by looking through a God-Jesus-Love filter as the *Course* does, for instance, or through various means of consciousness exploration—but you are always at the center of your I-universe. Okay, you killed me. We can do this again, but I'm done for now."

Thirty-Eight More Ways to Say
the Same One Thing

Men talk about Bible miracles because there is
no miracle in their lives. Cease to gnaw that crust.
There is ripe fruit over your head.

H.D. Thoreau

A FEW DAYS LATER, Maggie, Maya and I are exploring an old logging road on the other side of the mountain. During the walk, I tell Maggie about a stub trail going to the top of a nearby waterfall I hadn't checked out yet. Big mistake. The stub was a mile and a half of hard going, then it got real hard for the last quarter mile. The return trip was no picnic either.

"Do you know what orienteering is?" I ask Maggie during the descent.

"Sure," she says, surprising me, "running around in the woods with a map and compass, like a checkpoint race. We did something like that in Indian Maids."

"Indian Maids? Is that racist or sexist?"

"Probably both. It was like Girl Scouts but less dorky. Are you interested in orienteering?"

"I used to do it. I was wondering if you'd heard of anything like that around here."

"No, but I'm sure you can run around in the woods on your own. When I was in Indian Maids, I always thought it was dumb to do it in the woods. I said we should do it in DC or Atlanta, carry real hatchets and learn some real skills."

"Well," I say, "there's your movie."

✿

We get back to the cabin and I collapse on the couch as if someone cranked up the gravity. Maya only makes it halfway onto her bed. Maggie remains bright and energetic.

"Want to do some more of the list?" she asks after a few minutes.

"We can try," I mumble and struggle back into motion. I manage to get my shoes and socks off and get us some water. I set out some hummus and pita but I'm too tired to chew. The cabin is in the mid-sixties and doesn't really need a fire, but I get it going anyway so we have something to look at. Maggie puts her backpack up on the table and sets her stuff out. After ten minutes we're both settled in; me in my happy chair, Maggie on the couch with a laptop and a lap desk and a lap blanket, Maya still halfway on her bed.

13-33 - MIRACLES OUT OF TIME

"Ready?" Maggie asks.

"Let 'er rip."

"Okay," she says, "we're on thirteen. It says miracles are both beginnings and endings."

She leaves it hanging like I'm supposed to know what it means.

"Am I supposed to know what that means?"

"Uh," she continues, "they're affirmations of rebirth, they alter temporal order. They undo the past to change the future, I guess."

"Show me, please."

She brings the page and points to the thirteenth item. I read and hand it back to her.

"Yes, okay, that's right, but again, either the speaker has a weak grasp, or is dumbing it down for the intended audience."

"Which is why it's good that you're translating it," she says.

"I'm not making that leap," I say, "but okay. It means miracles occur outside of time. Time is subordinate to thought which, I guess, isn't obvious. Like, even if you think it's too late for something to happen, it can still happen. Universal mind is not stuck with the false limitations that define ego. Don't sweat the details, might be a better way of putting it. Just play your part and let things work. Don't worry about what's possible because you have no idea."

"Okay, so that was pretty good. Next one, fourteen, do miracles bear witness to truth?"

"Is there more?"

"It says miracles are convincing because they arise from conviction."

"Show me, please."

She brings it over and I read fourteen, and then scan down.

"It looks like the list might start devolving at this point. Fourteen isn't good, fifteen is bad, sixteen, seventeen, eighteen, nineteen, all weak. Twenty, no good, twenty-one, twenty-two, bad. Maybe I'm just being lazy, but these are just too tangled up to mess with. Twenty-three is, let's see, miracles rearrange perception, what does that mean? Sounds like wrong-knowing. Put levels in perspective… sickness comes from confusing the levels… uh, that might almost be something, but not quite."

"Twenty-four is about healing the sick and raising the dead," Maggie says. I read it a few times and want to like it more than it will let me. You're a creator, it says, and everything else is a dream. Kind of, maybe.

"This whole list speaks to a very juvenile understanding," I say. "Again, why wallow in muck when you can just climb out of it? Why lay in bed dreaming about waking up when you can just open your eyes? And if you don't want to wake up, what's the point of any of it? Moving on, twenty-five is too much to untangle, but it's the first time the list mentions atonement. I'm not sure what that means. Let's see, twenty-six might be something."

"Freedom from fear?"

"Maybe, in the sense that the sleepstate could be called the Fear Paradigm and the waking state could be called the Agapé Paradigm. It says atoning means undoing, and undoing of fear is an essential part of the atonement value of miracles, which can only mean undoing ego, so atonement might mean rebirth. Some of this makes more sense in that light, but it's still a stretch."

"I thought this whole list would be good," she says.

"It's very good if you want to understand how people get tricked into remaining in a state of childhood, but you need an adult perspective to understand it that way. Let's keep going."

Maggie settles onto the arm of my chair and we read the list together.

"Twenty-seven is the first time the author claims to be Jesus, but isn't really saying anything. Twenty-eight isn't bad; release from fear, again. Open your eyes and the scary dream is over."

"Miracles are a means, revelation is an end," Maggie reads.

"Weak, but not wrong," I say. "The use of focused intent to bring about the transition to adulthood is certainly valid, whether that's what it means or not."

"So that's pretty good, then."

"Well, we're not grading the list, we just want to see what's of value to the journey, like rifling through a stuffed back-pack and keeping only what's essential. If this list has what the journey requires, then it's useful, but a lot of it is excess. You need a small canteen and they give you a massive earthenware jug covered in runes."

"Your commentary elevates it," she observes.

"You're not writing," I observe.

"My laptop is recording, like I do for lectures. I'll get it turned into good notes. Don't worry, keep going."

"Okay, the last part of twenty-nine is good; miracles heal because they direct one from flesh to spirit. Thirty, same thing; spirit, perception, proper alignment, placing spirit at the center... I don't know, it's like trying to separate an ounce of sugar from a pound of salt. Thirty-one starts okay, miracles should inspire gratitude, not awe. Gratitude would be my preferred word for Agapé, so I like that. The rest of thirty-one kind of spins off into the whackosphere without being distinctly wrong. Thirty-two I guess is the author speaking as God or Jesus which I don't want to mess with, although the part about placing you above physical laws into a perfect state is okay-ish. Thirty-three starts bad but gets better. It says miracles dispel illusions and reveal the light in you, so that's not bad. It says that by releasing your mind from the imprisonment of illusions, sanity is restored, which is almost a clear and concise statement."

"That sounds pretty good, right?"

"Some of it is very good, just a little hard to cut through."

She takes the pages back to her seat and spends a few minutes writing.

34, 35 - The Symptoms of Blindness

"Dirty-dog," says Maggie, "pickles retard pimento dillness. Was Satan playing lip organ?"

"Jesus," I say, "what?"

"Thirty-four," she repeats, "miracles restore the mind to fullness. Does that mean waking up again?"

"Oh," I say, rubbing my eyes and shaking my head. "Sure, since they are intrinsically eye-opening, they reveal the pattern level of being. Once you start seeing this underlying reality more and more, physical reality seems less and less solid."

"It also says a mind restored to fullness is protected from intrusions."

"That sounds like the *Tao* thing; he who knows how to live has no place for death to enter, something like that. We used it in one of the books. The *Gita* has a thing too, chapter two, weapons can't cut it or fire burn it or wind make it dry, same general idea."

"I thought you had a good memory."

"Only for things I remember."

"We'll fix it in post."

"The *Course* is promoting the idea of a personal immortal soul, which doesn't exist, so that's more religious fat that needs to be trimmed. What did thirty-three say? Release your mind from the imprisonment of illusions and restore sanity. That's good. The author should follow his own advice."

"Okay, thirty-five says miracles don't always have observable effects."

"Not always visible to us, yes, that's very important. It means we shouldn't suppose ourselves qualified to judge. That's ego at work, thinking itself capable of seeing and understanding more than it can. In a lesser sense, no, you don't always see everything that's going on, or understand what you do see, but the larger sense is the trust in the process that releases you from doubt and distrust. This is actually very central to the whole thing. Your eyes are either open or closed, one or the other. Surrender and trust do not come from faith or belief, but from clear-seeing. The eyes-closed state is naturally panicky and distrustful and literally requires blind faith, but when you open your eyes and see how everything works, then distrust disappears and faith is forgotten. To concern yourself with results would be a symptom of blindness causing you to assume that *you* know better, that *your* will should be done, that *you* are the charioteer. But the main thing is to address the cause, not the symptoms. Open your eyes and the symptoms of blindness all disappear."

"That's interesting," she says, "that it's not a faith thing."

"Right, there's no faith or belief involved. Nothing is hidden or withheld. If you can see where you are and how things work, you don't need to believe anything."

36, 37 - The Alignment of Perception

"Thirty-six is good," says Maggie, "you'll like this one. Miracles come from right-thinking, from aligning your perception with truth, it says. That's right, isn't it?"

"Overlooking the misuse of the word truth, that's pretty good. The only valid objective of the spiritual journey is to bring yourself into alignment with the universe, so right-thinking and alignment are the core idea. Next one?"

"Oh boy," she says and hands me the page. I scan through thirty-seven and see her point. Too heavily encrusted in barnacles to be worth cleaning.

"I'll just rephrase the last part," I say, "which basically says that until you open your eyes, you can't detect what I call pattern and they call divine order. I'll also say that it's a little hinky that they're demonizing untruth. That demonstrates a critical misunderstanding of the purpose and perfection of the dreamstate. It's a misunderstanding to paint the dream-state as bad and Atman as good, but it's very common."

I scan the remainder of the list and decide to make a final sprint for the finish line.

"I'm just gonna run through the rest of these," I say. "You ready?"

"Go ahead."

I hold the sheet of paper up to the light and look through the rest of the list. It takes time to parse each item, play with possible translations, and weigh the effort required to make sense of any given statement against any possible benefit.

38-50 - BIG PICTURE RIGHTNESS

"Okay, thirty-eight is introducing a new character I don't recognize. Thirty-nine says that by perceiving light, darkness automatically disappears, which is surprisingly straightfor-ward. Forty is a greeting card. Forty-one might say that when you open your eyes, you perceive big picture rightness instead of small picture wrongness, so fine. Forty-two says something similar; free yourself and the symptoms of captiv-ity vanish. We seem to be interpreting miracle as waking up now, I didn't notice when that happened. Maybe with number twenty-five when it started talking about atonement."

"Atonement means becoming lucid?" she asks.

"According to whoever wrote this, maybe. Forty-three says if you're receptive, you can receive. Forty-four is something about Christ I can't translate. Forty-five is based on false-knowledge, so it's disqualified. Forty-six is, uh, worth some effort, actually. It says that miracles are just training wheels and when you learn to ride you don't need them anymore. That means that when you develop the spiritual sense, or what they're calling divine revelation, you don't need clumsy methods of interface anymore. That's very good."

I pause while she writes and continue when she looks up.

"Forty-seven is worded poorly but the idea is that miracles aren't subject to our conception of time, which I thought we already said. Forty-eight says that miracles are the only device at our disposal for controlling time, which is a weird way to say it, but close enough. Then it says revelation, the spiritual sense, transcends miracles because it has nothing to do with time. I want to agree with that, but I don't think I do. Forty-nine can be read two different ways; one is wrong, and the one that might be right is based on wrong-knowing. We could get bogged down in that but let's not. And finally, fifty has something to do with creation and alignment which, like a lot of this list, may or may not make sense."

"Wow, we're done!"

"Well, I'm sure we skipped through it too quickly and didn't treat the material with the respect it deserves, but it's like trying to translate a garbled transmission; you can make out bits and pieces, but it's mostly just static."

"Maybe the channel was bad," Maggie suggests. "Maybe it got all blurry as it came through the channel and no one has ever understood it well enough to fix it."

"Possibly, I didn't look at it in that light and I doubt I'll look at it again. It's important to remember that there's no one above us; no one has more knowledge than we have, no one can think better than we can think. Whether it's Jesus or some other supposedly ascended entity doesn't matter;

authorship does not confer authority. The only true authority comes from being right, and however right this list is, it's
mostly wrong."

"I guess that makes sense."

"I did get the impression that the list was evolving as it went,
like more and more it was saying that the main purpose of
miracles is to aid the transition to the integrated state. That
began with principle twenty-eight when it said miracles are a
means, revelation is an end. If so, I agree. Integration is not
the only use of the co-creative process, but for anyone in the
segregated state, I'd say it's the best."

"Do you think that's what people use it for?"

"No, probably health and wealth stuff, fear of lack, fear of
death."

"Was it worth going through the list with me? Do you
think you'll include this in your book?"

"I'm not sure yet. I'll write it out and see. It's a very long
way of saying something that can be said in a lot less words,
but it's also a good look at the subtle machinations of the
dreamstate and ego, at the hows and whys of obfuscation
and distortion. There's just enough accuracy in the list to
give it credence, to bait the trap, but then it packs it in layers
of religious dunnage which make it totally inaccessible to
anyone who might benefit from it. I would equate it with
Buddhism in its power to lure people in and hang onto
them. Within the context of the dreamstate, this a critically
important function. Consider the challenges of restricting a
healthy, intelligent population to a pre-pubescent developmental stage; it's really a masterwork of ingenuity.

❖

"I just thought of something," says Maggie.

"That's how it begins," I say.

"Jedvaita!" she announces grandly.

"Jed what now?"

"Jedvaita. Like Jedvaita Vedanta. That's what this book and *Theory of Everything* really are, right? Like you're taking Advaita and stripping out all the excess. That's what Aletheology really is, right? Jedvaita."

"No."

"You wrote the first three books, and that was the enlightenment trilogy. Now you wrote *Theory* and *Play* and *Dreamstate*, and that's like the dreamstate trilogy, right? So both trilogies make up Jedvaita. Pretty awesome, right?"

"No."

"Should I get the domain name? Jedvaita dot com?"

"No."

"Aren't you worried someone else will get it and pretend they're you?"

"No."

"Aren't you worried about people stealing your teachings and messing them up?"

"No."

"Will you at least say in the book that I thought of Jedvaita? Are you even listening to me? Jed? Jed? Are you dead, Jed? Oh well, Jed is dead. Good thing we harvested his mind fruit in time. Okay, Maya, my sweet, you can eat him now. Start with the little toesies and work your way up, but save the brain for tomorrow. Remember, my dear, the rule is; brain tomorrow and brain yesterday, but never brain today."

The Meaning of Creation

All matter originates and exists only by virtue of a force.
We must assume behind this force the existence of a
conscious and intelligent Mind. This Mind is the matrix
of all matter.

Max Planck

MAGGIE SPENDS THE NEXT half-hour writing, then starts talking half to me, half to herself.

"This whole thing is pretty weird. I mean, here's this book, the *Course*, and it's so respected and such a big deal and all these smart people are really into it, but to you it's just a dusty artifact from some ancient civilization and you're explaining their quaint belief systems and how primitive and superstitious they were. But it's not an ancient civilization, it's *this* one and I'm a part of it. And even saying *that* is just my primitive belief system talking, isn't it?"

I've been aware that, between her mother and me, Maggie must feel like the odd man out. Her mother is something of an alien to her and, in Maggie's eyes, I might be her mother's alien abductor. This isn't a pronounced thing and I have observed their relationship and found it to be particularly strong, but what do I know? The fact is that Maggie is trying to figure out who she is, and now she's spending the summer with her mother, who is something else, and a family friend, who is something else again. I can see where that might be a lot for a young person to deal with, but she has remained very centered throughout.

"Well, yes and no," I reply to her semi-rhetorical question. "When you stop labeling things good and bad, right and wrong, then you start to understand everything in terms of entertainment value."

"I'm not sure how entertained I am by all this," she says.

"Maybe it's more about us as creations than creators. From the perspective of Brahman, we ourselves are the point of creation. Our own downstream creations—art, technology, civilizations, belief systems and so forth—are only entertaining to Brahman insofar as they ignite our passions and make us more interesting to behold. In short, Brahman experiences creation as us, so our process of creation is more entertaining than the product of our creation."

"How do you know that?"

"I don't know anything, I'm just trying to put the pieces together so they fit, and that's how they fit."

❖

"I'm a little disappointed in the list," she says. "I thought it would be better."

"Taken on its own merits, it's surprisingly good. Understood from within the sleeping dreamstate, looking at it as a sort of New Age-Christian mashup, I'd say it's top notch. If I were into God and Jesus and Love, and wanted to really hit it hard, I'd dedicate myself to the *Course* over the Bible. Not much of it was distinctly wrong, the cleanup just needed more patience than I had to give."

"What about for me? Would I be interested in it?"

"You could try, but you'd quickly discover a mechanical incompatibility between you and the *Course,* and you'd drop it. But that's no reason not to try, if you felt like it."

She finishes writing, turns to a fresh page, and looks up.

"Would you like to make a closing statement?"

"Uh, maybe so, while it's still fresh. The *Course* is somewhat unique with*in* the spiritual marketplace, but it's perfectly typical *of* the spiritual marketplace. It serves the same purpose as any of it. In the dreamstate, right is wrong and wrong is right. Ego is necessary and illusion is of the essence. Some people are overly fond of reason, which can be disruptive to neutral buoyancy, so they're egically encouraged to stay in the safe zone. It's fear that does the encouraging, and all fear is ego's fear of no-self. That's why, when you detach from ego, you leave fear behind. Ego doesn't want to get shifted out of its comfort zone, and that's the problem that spiritual solutions like the *Course* actually solve; they provide us with a safe way to vent our freedom urge. There are no locks in this asylum, but there are many other ways of keeping us in. People get lured into something like the *Course* and spend their most vital years trying to follow its teachings, but when those years have passed, there they are, sitting at the bottom of a hole they could have easily climbed out of, but now their wad is shot and they're content with life in the hole."

I pause to let Maggie catch up with her notes.

"Something like this might have worked on me," I continue, "I might have taken all my focused energy and channeled it into some tail-chasing time-killer like Zen or Advaita or the *Course*. What I'm describing is like an invisible forcefield; it's very common, very effective, and it's the sole purpose of all religion and spirituality. Contentment is containment. Discontent creates change, which is the enemy of the sleep-state. There are many layers of protective restraint to keep us from doing what comes most naturally to a sentient being; being sentient."

✿

"Hold on," she says. "My laptop died and my hand is cramping up." She rubs her hands and shakes them out. "Okay," she says.

"Now," I continue, "here's something that wasn't mentioned in that list. There are no gaps in pattern. Wherever you go, wherever you look, it's always complete. Maybe the act of looking is an act of creation, who knows. So it's there when we look, but what about when we're not looking? The universe is like the box with Schrödinger's cat inside, but the real issue is not whether that cat is dead or alive, but whether the cat exists at all."

"Am I supposed to understand any of that?"

"Put a coin in a small box and shake it. Is the coin heads or tails?"

"We can't know until we open the box."

"Right. But there's an interpretation of quantum mechanics that says that, until we open the box and look, the coin is in a superposition of both heads and tails, and it's only when we open the box and look that the superposition collapses into a head or tail position."

"That doesn't sound right."

"That was Schrödinger's point. *Our* point is, how do we know there *is* a coin when the box is closed? If we open the box, we're sure we'll see the coin, but what's inside the box when we're not looking? That's the real tree-falls-in-a-forest question: Does anything exist unobserved? In a materialistic worldview, the answer is obviously yes, and in the dreamstate, it's obviously no, but in both cases, the answer is obviously unknowable. Even if we open the box and see the coin, we haven't answered the most fundamental question of all: Does creation exist? The answer is that there is no answer, which doesn't sound like an answer, but it really is. It's the answer to everything. It must be and it is."

"I don't have to understand any of this, right?"

"No one seems to."

"Okay, hold on, I'm writing. Okay."

"So that's what Schrödinger's cat is all about, it's the overstating of a simple koan: Does reality exist unobserved? And when we follow the question further, it becomes, Does reality exist when it *is* observed? Does reality exist at all?"

"So everything points to the dreamstate explanation."

"Nothing points away from it, and the materialistic view is only supported by belief based on appearances. The materialistic worldview is the accepted truth and the dreamstate is a zany hypothesis, but that should be reversed; reality-as-appearance should be the baseline and materialism is the bold hypothesis that should be defended or discarded. Material reality is just a hypothesis until proven. Any serious scientist would be on my side."

"But material reality can never be proven, right?"

"Right, apparent reality is validated by consensus, but since the facts only support reality as appearance, consensus can't be admitted as a supporting argument, leaving no support for the materialistic worldview at all. That's why consensus reality is insupportable and the dreamstate interpretation is the true baseline."

"Wow," she says after a burst of writing, "we really veered off-track."

"We just stayed on the track to see where it went. All spokes lead back to the same hub, which is the singularity; infinite consciousness. Truth."

"Nuts," she says, making her notes, "I know I'm writing this down all wrong."

"We'll fix it in post."

❖

"Einstein once asked someone if he really believed the moon only exists when he looks at it. He was asking sarcastically, as if the answer were too obvious to merit serious consideration, but this is the most important question science can ask, and the answer is not obvious at all. Does existence exist? Is reality real? This question that Einstein was so eager to mock is, in fact, the science killer. Einstein was trying to defend the indefensible proposition that observation constitutes proof.

His question reveals the false foundation upon which all science rests, and illuminates the fact that science itself is just another belief system."

"Even if everyone observes the same moon?"

"The existence of other people is unsupported, so they can't provide support to something else. What we can do is remove belief from the equation and start fresh. The first question about reality is, is reality real? Does anything really exist? No one can ever answer that, so nothing beyond that point can ever be more than belief."

"But science works. They do all this awesome stuff."

"I'm not arguing with their ability to describe and harness the underlying perfection of the dreamstate, I'm arguing against their claim to understand it."

"Boy, you really have a thing for science and religion, don't you?"

"If you want to convince people to question their religion, you have to start by killing their gods and priests and defiling the corpses, which is actually a very amusing pastime."

✸

Had Einstein asked me if I believed that the moon only exists when I'm looking at it, I would have wondered why he felt the need to cast my argument in a ridiculous light; why he chose to erect a straw man and attack that instead of addressing the real question of whether or not there is such a thing as objective knowledge.

"It would be quite ridiculous of me to believe the moon only exists when I look at it," I would tell him.

"Just so," he might agree.

"In fact," I'd continue, "I believe the moon *does* exist in the same way I believe I am a person looking at it. The same way I believe you exist and time exists and watermelons exist. I don't have any proof of these things, but I believe them because this is reality and that's how it works. What I *don't* believe in is belief, and I would never be so cavalier with truth as to confuse it with appearances, Herr Professor."

"Please," he would say, "call me Al."

"But you, on the other hand," I'd continue, "are saying that you *know* the moon exists because you *see* it, which is a different matter entirely. The evidence of your senses may be fine for the purposes of life, but it hardly meets the standards of serious thought. My question to you is, based on what actual proof do you assert that the moon truly exists?"

"Obviously," Einstein would confess, donning his philosopher cap, "there can be no such proof."

He would then sniffle and move in for a hug, but I would step back.

"Of course not," I'd say. "Only consciousness itself can rise to that level. So we see that your belligerent moon question was only meant to compensate for the fact that your entire system of scientific validation is based on nothing more than hardened belief masquerading as science. Isn't that the truth?"

"Ja, ja," he'd blubber. *"Ich bin ein* big fat liar." Then he'd hand me his Nobel Prize and go out to get a normal haircut.

❧

In the course of our discussion of the principles of miracles, I have come to realize that Maggie has no great interest in the topic she approached me with. She knew I'd be here when she came home for the summer and she wanted to have something to share and discuss. She looked into it a bit and came to the conclusion that *A Course In Miracles* would be something she could use to engage with me, similar to our interactions in Mexico. The *Course* is around twelve hundred pages of material, though, so she confined herself to the list of principles to give us a manageable portion.

"So," I say to her, "not your roommate, I guess."

"No," she says, "well, kinda. She got me started on the *Course*, but I thought I was really onto something. The unreal does not exist, the real can't be threatened, right? I thought it was really, you know, something we could talk about. I tried discussing it with my mother first, but she just looked at me like I wasn't on the bus."

"It's not in books," I say.

"That's exactly what she said. It's not in books."

"Well, it was very thoughtful of you to make the effort. I hope it's been pleasant for you."

"I really like hanging out with you," she says, "but I'm wondering what I should be doing with all this."

"In my view, you're doing fine. Don't worry, there are no mistakes. Be patient. Give yourself time to discover your inner vision."

"My inner vision?"

"You jump out of a plane two or three miles up, and your drop zone is just a couple of small lines on a big chunk of Earth. You jump and it's crazy, you're going like, what, a hundred twenty-something miles an hour, wind deafening, maybe not too graceful at first, maybe a little in shock about leaping into a vast emptiness, but then you get a handle on it and enjoy the ride, right? You don't even care where you're supposed to land at this point, you're just having fun and trying to remember not to die. You get a couple of minutes of that, then you're down to where you pop your chute and *bam!*, rapid deceleration. That's a jarring experience, but now you're floating under canopy, pretty safe. Now you see where you're supposed to go and you can steer yourself in. It started out pretty wild, but you knew roughly where you were going from a good altitude so now you can circle in and literally land on a dime. That's the journey you're on right now, but you're still in the crazy and not very graceful part. Have fun with it. You can afford to be a little reckless. You have a main and a reserve, so it's a good time to do stupid stuff and try new things. The time will come to pop your chute and enter the next phase of the ride. Is any of this making sense?"

"Not really," she scowls. "I thought you were supposed to be good at this."

"I'm a little out of practice, and life advice was never my thing. The point is, you use that first stage, where you are now, to more or less discover your sense of where you want to go with this whole thing. You've got that whole planet below you and you can land anywhere. That's where you develop your own vision, and what elevates certain people above the herd is depth and clarity of their vision. Take your time to figure that part out, is what I guess I'm saying, and then, to answer your question, you'll know what you should be doing with all this. Until you have a vision to pursue, your job is to discover your vision. Most people never do, so they walk in circles and die with their music still in them, so to speak.

Find your vision and then every step will be a step toward its realization. If you want something, it's enough that you focus on it and steer toward it. That will create an unfolding, and as you get closer you'll start seeing what it really is that you really want; your authentic desire as opposed to an egoic desire. That's what miracles really are; the dynamic co-creative interaction that transcends false ideas of self and non-self. That's why they seem miraculous from the segregated perspective and ordinary from the integrated perspective. Make a movie, carve a walking stick, kill the pope, play the piano, it's all the same. You desire, you act, the universe responds. Try figuring out what you *don't* want and release it. That might be the more important part of the process; achieving rightness through the hacking away of wrongness."

"You make it all sound so simple."

"It is and it's not. People contain layers of complexity beyond reckoning. Every life is a unique combination of obstacle and obstruction, but just as we all experience gravity and sunshine, so do we all have access to the inner dimension that is the very nature of self-awareness. I can't lead anyone out of their personal maze of identity and circumstance, but I know what they'll find when they find their way out."

"I know it all makes sense and everything," she says, "but it's hard to think of reality as not being real. Like, how can none of this really exist? That's just too weird. I don't disagree with anything you say, but I could still never really believe it."

"Same for me. Reality seems as real to me as it does to you. If I kick a rock, I break a toe."

"But you're saying it's all a dream."

"As sager sages say, reality neither exists nor doesn't. Don't think in terms of how real reality seems, think of how meaningful it is. You are not immortal, you are going to die. Meaning doesn't exist, and if there's no meaning, then what's real about anything? It has nothing to do with how solid matter seems, it has to do with understanding that, regardless of any other consideration, life is totally pointless. Nothing lasts, nothing you do matters, and nothing can change that. Your insignificance is absolute. No-self is true self. This is the lesson of impermanence. You begin with a blank slate, you create your mandala, then you sweep it away. I know impermanence sounds kind of dreary, but it's the truth, and there's not a lot of that going around."

"The truth shall set you free, I guess."

"Okay, but what do you want with freedom? Wrigley Field in Chicago is called the Friendly Confines. That's what the dreamstate is, the friendly confines. Why would you want to escape from that, and where would you go? You're like a character in the friendly confines of a holodeck. You can't leave, but you can be awake to your situation; you don't have to be deceived and two-dimensional like the other characters you see. You can understand what and where you are and take full advantage of all the wonders of holodeck technology. You create whatever you want to create, and, in so doing, you create yourself. What we're talking about is how to hack the system. You and the ship's computer are co-creating your holodeck reality. You are a manifestation of the computer; it is mind and you are mind. Same thing, right? There's no meaning to any of it, and there's nowhere else to go, but so what? You live, you play your role, you dream a life. You pop up out of nowhere, strut and fret your hour upon the holodeck, full of sound and fury signifying nothing, and then are heard no more. It's that or nothing, so it's really a pretty good deal. Do what you want really *is* the whole of the law. Dream well, and make your dream come true. If you authentically want to make a movie, make it happen. Be specific, don't make it an egoic desire like 'I want to be a movie maker.' Make it something specific like, 'I am going to bring this exact project to the screen or die trying.' Focus on what you really want, then start manifesting the shit out of it and watch as the universe reshapes itself to you; that's where the truly miraculous stuff comes into play, and there's really nothing spiritual or esoteric about any of it, it's just the way things work. Clarity of vision is the animating principle of the dreamstate, the seed at the heart of any endeavor. Magic isn't when you wiggle your nose and something appears, it's when you shine focused emotional energy through an idea and project it from a thought in your head to a thing in the world, which is really just a thought in a bigger head. Anything anyone has ever done was done exactly this way. Sometimes the process is random or vague and the results are sketchy, sometimes the process is highly refined and the results are a testimony to the infinite potential of the co-creative dreamstate. Look around at where you are and what you're a part of. It's an infinite dream machine where you can create anything you can imagine. Take a step back, one small step, and really see what people can do; in art and science and religion, in politics and sports, in exploration and war. Look at societies and civilizations, cities and nations, all born of the masculine and feminine energies, intelligence and emotion, focus and intent, yin and yang. The accomplishments of man are endlessly fascinating, and they are all accomplished under false pretenses. Everything anyone has ever done, they've done for a lie. The lie itself doesn't matter—God, glory, posterity, heaven, greed, love, hate—all fear-based, all exactly the same. The only thing that matters is what gets created in the name of the lie. What is your life but your own self-portrait? Your own one-man show? Now here you are, ready to begin the creative adventure of your life, and no matter what you do, your greatest creation will always be yourself. The combination of focus and intent is the key to everything. Heart and mind. Nothing was ever created any other way. Discover your vision, then pour your life into it and you will materialize it, not because of some cheesy miracle formula, but because creation is the essential function of the dreamstate. Creation is itself the meaning of creation; that's the closest thing to meaning there is. It's not true, but who gives a shit about truth? Have fun, make a mess, don't worry about breaking anything. It's your universe, do with it as you wish. Make sense?"

"Hold on a sec," she says, struggling to keep up.

"Okay," she says, checking back over her notes. "Let's see. So I said the truth shall set you free, and then you said what again?"

Good Enough Is Good Enough

The world is like a ride in an amusement park, and when
you choose to go on it you think it's real because that's
how powerful our minds are. The ride goes up and down,
around and around, it has thrills and chills, and it's very
brightly colored, and it's very loud, and it's fun for a while.
Many people have been on the ride a long time, and they
begin to wonder, "Hey, is this real, or is this just a ride?"
And other people have remembered, and they come
back to us and say, "Hey, don't worry, don't be afraid, ever,
because this is just a ride."

Bill Hicks

T HERE IS WITHIN EACH OF US both God and Brahman
because we are each both performer and spectator. God
is created in our image and loves the quiet life, but we are
created in the image of Brahman so we crave high drama
and plenty of thrills. We are divided between our roles of
drama-loving beholder and comfort-loving beheld; we wish
to sleep peacefully but dream amusingly.

Our Gods may judge between good and evil, but Brahman judges between amusing and boring. Just as your game avatar or favorite cartoon character takes a beating to keep you amused, so might you take a few lumps for the amusement of your upstream audience. Naturally, we don't wish to suffer, but boring the audience is the greatest sin that can be committed in the theater, and that's all the dreamstate really is.

❁

In closing, let us speak in praise of ego. Let us behold the works of ego and marvel at the sprawling epic which ego hath wrought upon the grand stage of the dreamstate theater.

Here we find the living *Mahabharata*—the great story of man, the one story which contains all others—and ego is the magic spark without which we'd all just be Kens and Barbies in Maya's dollhouse. We are quick to denounce ego as untrue, but this marvellous palace would just be an empty box without it. Ego is the magic that brings the dreamstate to life.

Compare the history of man on Earth to the history of Earth before man and you'll see what a difference ego makes. This one small planet is home to an incomprehensibly rich and diverse tapestry of drama and creativity of which the rest of the known universe is utterly devoid. And even if there are other theaters out there somewhere, they too are ego-based because that's the only way it works. Ego is the lie that makes the world go 'round. Ego is why we strut and fret, and it is to ego that we must be grateful for our hour upon the stage.

❁

Although you do exist in truth, the character you play, the person you think you are, does not. No-self is true self. You are not real and reality is not real; it's all just empty spectacle as the certain impossibility of meaning proves beyond all argument. But all the logic in the world can't change the simple fact that when you kick a rock, you break your toe, and a broken toe feels awfully goddamn real. The dreamstate might not be *really* real, but it's *pretty* real, and whatever else we might say about it, it's a hell of a lot more amusing than truth.

The Thought of Honey

*A man is walking in a dark, dangerous forest, filled with
wild beasts. The forest is surrounded by a vast net. The man is
afraid, he runs to escape from the beasts, he falls into a pitch
black hole. By a miracle, he is caught in some twisted roots.
He feels the hot breath of an enormous snake, its jaws wide
open, lying at the bottom of the pit. He is about to fall into
these jaws. On the edge of the hole, a huge elephant is about to
crush him. Black and white mice gnaw the roots from which
the man is hanging. Dangerous bees fly over the hole letting
fall drops of honey… Then the man holds out his finger—
slowly, cautiously—he holds out his finger to catch the drops of
honey. Threatened with so many dangers, with hardly a breath
between him and so many deaths, he still has not reached
indifference. The thought of honey holds him to life.*

The Mahabharata, Jean-Claude Carrière

Printed in Great Britain
by Amazon